CREATING POSITIVE FUTURES

First published January 2007
Reprinted January 2012

Published by BT Press
17 Avenue Mansions, Finchley Road, London NW3 7AX
www.btpress.co.uk
+44 (0)20 7794 4495

Designed by Alex Gollner

ISBN 978-1-871697-79-7

CREATING POSITIVE FUTURES

SOLUTION FOCUSED RECOVERY
FROM MENTAL DISTRESS

Lucie Duncan   Rayya Ghul   Sarah Mousley

Contents

Acknowledgements

Lucie, Rayya and Sarah would like to thank the following people from the occupational therapy world: Sylvia Cuthbert Head OT, South East Kent NHS Trust, for her faith and support in getting this project off the ground. Lynn Hatton for her adminstrative support. South East Kent (NHS) Trust for allowing us to pilot the Measure and giving us time to work on the project. All the occupational therapists who piloted the Measure and gave us valuable feedback. John Puddle, Paul Mousley, Simon Hannaford and Ailsa Gillen for those little tips that made all the difference. Cathy Kingham and Ian Marsh for reading the book and providing useful comments. Alan Duncan for the photographs.

From the solution focused world:

All at the Brief Therapy Practice, in particular Chris Iveson who encouraged us to consider writing a book in the first place, provided support and suggestions and never lost faith in us. Rayya would like to thank Brian Cade, Paul Z. Jackson, Mark McKergow and Harry Norman who made her feel she had something to offer, not just to learn.

And most importantly our families for their patience and support.

This book is dedicated to Dr. Mahmud Ghul, Robin Tandy, Dr. Thomas Dalton and Rosemary Dalton.

...and to the four babies who were born to Lucie and Sarah during the time it took us to write the book: Millie, Jack, Ella and Jim.

FOREWORD

Brian Cade

This book has been written by three occupational therapists and reflects their varied professional experiences. It will however be a valuable resource for anybody working in the fields of mental health and disability regardless of professional discipline, including not only occupational therapists but also psychiatrists, psychologists, social workers and nurses.

It describes and demonstrates a respectful, structured and realistically optimistic way of talking with troubled people such that their own strengths and resources are highlighted, and focused towards discovering practical ways of surmounting difficulties and dealing more effectively with their lives. However, in contrast to many approaches, the accent is heavily placed on ways of eliciting the client's ideas about what will improve things rather than promoting the professional's ideas. As Blaise Pascal wrote back in the seventeenth century, "People are generally better persuaded by the reasons which they have themselves discovered than by those which have come into the minds of others." A structured approach is elaborated which is based around a way of talking with clients that highlights their resources, and facilitates thinking differently about their future. As the neurologist Antonio Damasio pointed out, "Images of something that has not yet happened and that may in fact never come to pass are no different in nature from the images you hold of something that already has happened. They constitute the memory of a possible future rather than of the past that was."

Much of this book is devoted to the *Solution Focused Measure of Occupational Function* which the authors define as "...a semi-structured interview tool, which encourages collaboration between a client and the therapist." They draw an important distinction between occupation and activity. The former includes the real-life experiences of daily living which give people a sense of continuity and normality, and exist only in relation to the person carrying them out. The latter are graduated tasks, often standardised, carried out as exercises in skill, prescribed by a worker in order to make an assessment. They use the example of making a cup of tea. In an occupational therapy kitchen it is a monitored activity, whereas making a cup of tea just the way you've always liked it in your own kitchen at home is an occupation.

This book is clearly written and almost jargon-free. It contains many useful case-examples and suggestions for generative questions, and the authors have avoided it becoming too much of a therapy-by-numbers "cook-book". I strongly recommend it.

Brian Cade
Brief and Family Therapist
Private Practice, Sydney, Australia
Primary author of *A Brief Guide to Brief Therapy*

INTRODUCTION

Rayya Ghul

In recent years, mental health service users have suggested that, as experts in their own experiences of being and living, they could perhaps be trusted to know what they want and need. Professionals working in mental health services could then be useful allies and collaborators in finding ways through the trickier aspects of living that clients experience. This is hard to do when mental distress is generally defined as a medical problem requiring a medical solution.

Mental illness, as conceived by medicine, is a problem requiring a solution. Those in mental distress are described as 'people with mental health problems', which suggests that in order to help them, all we need to do is solve a set of problems. This immediately poses the question: who defines the problems and determines what the ideal solutions might be? There is, of course, nothing wrong with problem-solving. However, the result is just that: a solution to a particular problem. For example, some doctors may see mental health problems in terms of chemical imbalances that require correction with medication. Some in society may see only 'mad' people who need to be locked up for the safety of others.

The solution focused approach liberates both service user and therapist from the constraints inherent in traditional approaches to problem-solving. Instead, it offers the possibility that each interaction between service user and therapist is an exploration of possible futures for someone trying to lead the best possible life. It is a radical approach to working in mental health and much more than a new method of problem-solving.

This book describes examples of working in a solution focused way within mental health services. Although it was written by occupational therapists it should be useful to any profession working with people in short or long-term mental distress. When we started writing this book in 2001, the idea of service user empowerment and involvement was in its infancy in mainstream British services. Now, a slow but insistent shift of power is taking place. Service users are becoming recognised as 'experts in experience' and there is a gradual dawning that effective services can only arise from collaboration and negotiation.

Central to this is the 'recovery' movement which provides a new narrative of living with shifting mental states and episodes of mental distress. Rather than viewing a person as lessened or limited through illness, the focus is on seeing that someone can continue to live, develop and flourish even when the illness is not 'cured'. Anthony *(1993, in Roberts & Wolfson, 2004)* defines recovery as:

> "a deeply personal, unique process of changing one's
> attitudes, values, feelings, goals, skills and roles. It is a
> way of living a satisfying, hopeful, and contributing life
> even with limitations caused by the illness. Recovery
> involves the development of new meaning and purpose
> in one's life as one grows beyond the catastrophic effects
> of mental illness." *(p39)*

Throughout this book we hope you will see how the solution focused approach may well be the ideal one for responding to the recovery movement. It is fundamentally an approach of hopefulness. We see clients as resourceful and talented and holding the key to their own recovery. We believe that, given the opportunity, people respond to the challenge of setting their own priorities, pursuing their own interests and having the chance to grow beyond the limited expectations of traditional mental health practice. The ideas in this book demonstrate some of the ways that this can be supported through careful listening and creating a positive focus through conversation. Using a solution focused approach has made it easy for us to feel optimistic about our clients and their chosen futures.

Occupational therapists have a great deal to offer mental health services. We are already accustomed to the idea that people can live fulfilled and productive lives despite chronic illness or disability, and we have a client-centred philosophy at the heart of our practice. Many of the examples in this book show how our understanding of everyday life informs the focus of our work. Increasingly, mental health services are being asked to look beyond diagnosis and symptoms and see the source of well-being as balance and competence in everyday activities. We therefore hope that it is not only the solution focused aspect of this book that will be useful to readers from different professions, but also the perspectives from occupational therapy.

Chapter One gives the reader an overview of solution focused brief therapy and provides transcripts of sessions to illustrate the types of conversation. At the end of the book there is a list of recommended books for readers who would like to learn more about the approach. Chapter Two introduces the Solution Focused Measure of Occupational Function and provides descriptions of how to use it with clients, as well as explanations and examples for each of the 25 questions. Chapter Three introduces a series of photocopiable worksheets that can be used on their own or in conjunction with the Measure. Chapter Four suggests ways that therapists can use the solution focused approach for their own continuing professional development. Lastly, Chapter Five contains transcribed case studies to illustrate how the Measure is used in practice, as well as how the information can be used to build a strengths-based report.

The authors' aim is that this book will provide a resource for all mental health professionals looking for ways to increase their effectiveness in client-centred practice. At the very least we hope that readers will try out the ideas and find them useful. At best we hope that the book contributes to ensuring that mental health service users are fully in control of their recovery.

Solution Focused Occupational Therapy?

Despite having grown out of different traditions at different times, occupational therapy and solution focused brief therapy appear to share some important guiding principles. The British definition of client-centred occupational therapy is:

- A partnership between the client and the therapist that empowers the client to engage in functional performance and fulfil his or her occupational roles in a variety of environments.
- The client participates actively in negotiating goals which are given priority and are at the centre of assessment.
- Throughout the process the therapist listens to and respects the client's values, adapts the interventions to meet the client's needs and enables the client to make informed decisions.
  (Sumsion, 2000)

The 'essence' of solution focused brief therapy is described by the Brief Therapy Practice as:

- To work with the person rather than the problem
- To look for resources rather than deficits
- To explore possible and preferred futures
- To explore what is already contributing to those possible futures
- To treat clients as the experts in all aspects of their lives
  (George, Iveson, Ratner, 1999)

Keilhofner states of the core values of occupational therapy:

"Deeply ingrained in occupational therapy is a belief in each person's essential humanity and worth irrespective of any impairments. This commitment has supported occupational therapists in their involvement with the most disabled and difficult patients and clients. This value has also shaped the strong tendency in occupational therapy to focus on the assets of individuals and to emphasise them in the therapeutic process. Closely tied to this humanistic perspective is the conviction that it is important to know and respect the unique perspective of the patient or client." *(Kielhofner, 1992)*

It can be seen that the main areas of similarity between solution focused brief therapy and occupational therapy are those regarding the client as the expert in his or her own life, and the focus on strengths and resources rather than problems or disabilities. It is therefore not surprising that both approaches operate from a collaborative stance.

Occupational therapy and solution focused brief therapy also share a view of humans as unique individuals. People are believed to be unique in the way they think about themselves, how they do things, how they make sense of the world and how they change. This does not mean that these differences are always great. Like the rest of nature there are recognisable patterns such as different kinds of tree; no two trees are the same, but we still recognise them as trees. Similarly, there are different kinds of teenager and no two are the same but we can broadly recognise patterns of behaviour as being those of a teenager.

Taking into account each client's unique perspective, both solution focused brief therapy and occupational therapy have become interested in the meanings clients ascribe to aspects of their life (for occupational therapists) and the way they talk about them (for solution focused brief therapists). Recent theorists in occupational therapy have stressed the importance of understanding occupation as meaningful and not simply as a set of activities or tasks.

For example, a client, John, with chronic pain syndrome and depression had become completely withdrawn from family life. He identified making a sandwich for his child's lunchbox as a first step goal. The following week the client reported that he had made the sandwich and then decided to make the sandwiches on three days the next week. John was delighted with his progress and in particular the response of his daughter.

The simple activity of making a sandwich was a success for John, not in the simple terms of competence or skill but in the profound meaning the activity has for him; the return to a parental role within his family. The common sense or layperson's view of occupation is that it is the activity life of a person; it is what they do. Occupation is viewed as a set of actions requiring different skill levels that can be learned and taught. While this is undoubtedly an important quality of occupation it does not take into account the human being who is carrying out the occupation. If we think again of the trees and teenagers, we see that people perform their occupations in a unique way.

A good occupational therapist knows that occupation is inherently purposeful and meaningful and they utilise this in therapy. John's therapist was willing to understand the meaning of sandwich-making for him (the client with chronic pain syndrome). She did not assume that he would be better off using his energy by going to the upstairs toilet. Conversely, an intervention, however well-reasoned, which is not meaningful for the client will not be effective. This is why many pieces of equipment lie unused in the homes of disabled people and why the in-patient in a mental health unit may not want to attend a pre-determined group programme. Occupation possesses 'a multidimensionality of an activity in context' *(Gray, 1998, p358)*. It refers to activities that are 'perceived as "doing"; pertaining to the client's sense of self; goal-directed, personally meaningful, and culturally and developmentally relevant' *(Christiansen, 1994, Clark et al, 1991, Gray, 1997 cited in Gray, 1998 p358)*. In other words it is the right activity, at the right time, in the right place. It is identified by the client as something that they need and value and is appropriate to their age and culture.

When this emphasis on meaning is taken into account, the way questions are framed and asked in solution focused brief therapy links closely into occupational therapy. The use of language as a therapeutic tool in interviews has not been extensively explored or written about in occupational therapy literature. However, there has been acknowledgement of this in writing on client-centred practice. Sumsion *(1999, p32)* states that 'The actions necessary to be truly client centred will not occur if the process does not begin with and continue to include the words that convey a commitment to this approach and the client's central role throughout the process.'

John's goal of making a sandwich was arrived at during a solution focused interview. He had been asked to talk about a time in his life when he felt things were going well. During this conversation he had identified a time when he was able to contribute to the family financially and emotionally. He had described this time in some detail and with some emotion associated with loss of that lifestyle. The therapist then asked, 'What would be the first small sign that your life was beginning to become more like that again?'

These 'signs' that the client searches for and highlights in the process of a solution focused interview are the meanings unique to their life. They are the (often unconscious) markers that tell us we are doing well in our aspirations, that we are on the right track. For people who have suffered trauma or disruption of their mental health, regaining a focus on these important signs can be the key to recovery or taking control of their lives. For many of our client this may be the first time that anyone has asked them what they want. Rather than viewing the client as being in the dark and the role of the therapist to provide a torch to light the way, working collaboratively in a solution focused approach means the therapist and client are in the dark together but with two torches.

Occupational therapy and solution focused brief therapy are each in their own right important contributions to the world of mental health work. Integrating the skills and ideas of solution focused work should enhance collaboration with our clients since the approaches share an important ideological common ground. Solution focused conversations allow the client to carry out their own occupational analysis through describing in detail what they will be doing when life is going well. For clients who do not require direct assistance with developing occupations, the occupational therapist may find that through using solution focused questioning, they are encouraging clients to take control of their own progress and that their role is more of coach than therapist.

Sometimes, however, conversation is not enough. The understanding that occupational therapy has of 'occupation' is enormously important to our practice and allows us to engage with clients with complex needs. For example, the occupational therapist knows how to grade and adapt occupations. This ensures that the client experiences success and challenge in a useful balance. A client who wants to learn computing skills may not be ready to go to college because of a lack of self-confidence or social skills following an episode of unstable mental health. In solution focused brief therapy the client is encouraged to identify small signs of progress towards their preferred future. In some areas of life, acting on this is not always possible. For example, enrolment on a course generally requires regular attendance and participation. Being able to attend a graded programme in a resource house or day service provides a good stepping-stone for the client to achieve their goal.

We are suggesting that solution focused brief therapy provides a frame of reference for using conversation as a therapeutic tool within all parts of the occupational therapy process from assessment to discharge. It also provides from the outset a way of engaging and respecting the client's perspective in clinical reasoning. These ideas are aimed at integrating and enhancing practice rather than replacing it.

Sumsion, *(1999, p32)* states that 'the application of a client-centred practice requires the adoption of a new language. Few new words are required but the pattern of word usage must be changed.' The authors believe solution focused brief therapy will be a significant contribution to this enterprise.

Development of the Solution Focused Measure of Occupational Function

The ideas shared in this book are the result of the authors' experiences of finding ways to integrate a solution focused approach with occupational therapy without compromising either. In 1999 Lucie Duncan and Sarah Mousley began to develop an interview assessment tool based on solution focused principles. They did the majority of the work on what has now become the Solution Focused Measure of Occupational Function, which is introduced in this book.

The Measure was further developed in collaboration with Rayya Ghul. At the end of 1999 the first version was piloted for three months by 25 occupational therapists working in mental health settings in what was then South East Kent Community Trust. At the end of the pilot the participating therapists completed a questionnaire regarding the perceived usefulness of the Measure, and suggestions for improvement were sought. The result of the pilot suggested that the Measure was seen as highly useful, easy to use and fitting well with existing occupational therapy practice. Changes to the Measure were made based on the suggestions received. Following the pilot, the second version of the Measure was distributed to the participating occupational therapists and the decision was made at management level to approve the Measure for use within the Trust, where it is now in regular use.

From 2002-5, the Measure was used as an assessed task within the second-year mental health course at Canterbury Christ Church University College. Students completed the Measure from a tape recorded interview and provided a formulation of the occupational performance needs of the 'client' in the case study. The exercise was completed twice each year (once as a practice and once as an assessment) by three cohorts of approximately 70 students, providing evidence for the consistency of results. Despite variations in the quality of the information, as would be expected from undergraduates, the content of the reasoning and analysis remained remarkably consistent for a sample of around 420 scripts. During this time, further changes were made to the Measure and the third and final version, which appears in this book, was completed.

CHAPTER ONE

A SOLUTION FOCUS

Rayya Ghul

The solution focused approach has its origin in Solution Focused Brief Therapy which was developed by Steve de Shazer and Insoo Kim Berg and their colleagues at the Brief Therapy Center in Milwaukee, USA, in the early 1980s. Since then, there has been considerable interest in the approach by health and social care professionals working in every conceivable setting with a huge variety of client groups all over the world. It was introduced into Britain by Evan George, Chris Iveson and Harvey Ratner while they were working together in an NHS child, family and adult psychiatric clinic in central London. They then set up the Brief Therapy Practice, the first solution focused brief therapy centre in the UK and offered training in the approach. While the majority of this book deals with applying a solution focus to working in mental health services, it will be useful first to look at solution focused brief therapy and its main components.

Solution focused brief therapy is a 'talking' therapy in that it takes place in the form of a conversation between therapist and client (or clients). Readers will be aware of other therapies such as cognitive behaviour therapy or psychodynamic psychotherapy. The main observable difference between these therapies is in the way that the therapist talks to the client; specifically, language is their tool. It may be an obvious point to make, but it is worth considering. The way a question is framed or phrased has a specific power and result. For example, in conversation with someone who has suffered abuse, asking 'How did you respond to what was happening?' will lead to a completely different conversation than 'How did what was happening affect you?' The reason is that the meaning of 'respond' indicates some sort of choice, power or locus of control, however limited. 'Affect' implies a passive experience where all the power is with the person or object that *affects* the person. These two conversations will be experienced differently by the client. Talking about responses is more likely to allow the client to discover signs of their strength and resources, rather than talking about effects which might reinforce the experience of being a victim.

The form of verbal communication used in various therapies reflects the focus of the therapy. For example, a cognitive behaviour therapist might ask, 'Just before you lose your temper in a traffic jam, what thought pops into your mind?' He or she is trying to elicit an automatic thought because they believe that by challenging these thoughts the client can change their behaviour. On the other hand, a psychodynamic psychotherapist might say, 'It's interesting that whenever you talk about your father, you use words that describe a battle.' The therapist is trying to encourage the development of insight because they believe this will help the client make changes. In both these cases, the questions are ways to engage the client in a process of psychological change based on the theoretical belief system of the therapist.

Traditional therapies have for the most part arisen from developing an idea of the 'healthy' person and then seeing the problems people experience as deviating from this ideal. Therapy is then designed to 'correct' this deviance back to the norm. Solution focused brief therapy does not diagnose, formulate or prescribe. It is, at its simplest, a conversation between therapist and client which in itself may help to provide a different experience of a problem and therefore uncover possible solutions that were not, and possibly could not, be considered previously. It acknowledges and utilises the dynamic and systemic aspects of human experience. This is not to say the solution focused brief therapy is somehow better than a therapy based on a normative model, but to highlight this fundamental difference. However, we believe this difference makes solution focused brief therapy closer to the paradigm of occupational therapy and therefore more congruent in practice.

In solution focused brief therapy there is no universal theory of human psychological function or therapeutic change. The therapist does not know which solutions will work with any given client. Instead there is an acknowledgement of difference between people. Everyone is unique in the way they think about themselves, how they do things, how they make sense of the world and how they change. Therefore the solution focused therapist doesn't believe they know *how* a given client will change or make changes as a result of their meeting. Instead they believe that talking about those desired changes in a specific way is more likely to help their clients' experience of life improve.

A good way of thinking about solution focused questions is to ask 'Will asking this question lead to a useful conversation?' Of course this begs the question: what does 'useful' mean? If we consider the 'essence' of solution focused brief therapy as suggested by the Brief Therapy Practice as:

- To work with the person rather than the problem
- To look for resources rather than deficits
- To explore possible and preferred futures
- To explore what is already contributing to these possible futures
- To treat clients as the experts in all aspects of their lives

(George, Iveson, Ratner, 1999)

A 'useful' conversation would be one that allows the above points to be achieved. As you consider the transcribed conversations in this book, it might be helpful to refer back to these points and consider how each question the therapist asks fits in with these statements.

The solution focused questions that lead to useful conversations fall into three broad categories:

- Preferred future questions
- Exception questions
- Scaling questions

In addition, to structure the interview the therapist will also make use of the following conversational aspects which are specific applications of the above questions. They conform to the definition of 'usefulness' in relation to the 'essence of solution focused brief therapy' as developed by the Brief Therapy Practice.

- Problem-free talk
- Pre-session change
- Coping questions
- Compliments/positive feedback

Goal-setting arises naturally out of the solution focus process, as will be seen.

Preferred Future

The solution focused brief therapist is interested in what their client wants from therapy and how this will change their life. All clients have some idea of how they would prefer their future to be, even if this is simply expressed as an absence of something such as unhappiness or discomfort. The questions the therapist may ask will encourage clients to think about this future in great detail, focusing on everyday experience rather than general goals. The answers have meaning for the client as a sign of life going well. While forming goals based on these answers can be useful, at this stage, identifying 'markers' of success is important. Clients often lose sight of these signs when they have suffered disruption of their life through mental and emotional distress. This contributes to the client's sense of loss of self or having lost control or direction in life. Asking questions which require the client to identify these signs can be grounding and provides a sense of being back on track.

Examples of such questions:

- How will you know that coming to see me was worthwhile? What difference will you see in yourself and your life?
- What will you see yourself doing differently when life is going well again?

The answers and conversations elicited by these questions will differ from client to client. The skill of the therapist lies in ensuring that the client has a clear picture of their preferred future which is expressed in concrete, positive terms. For example:

THERAPIST: What will you see yourself doing differently when life is going well again?

CLIENT: I won't be staying at home doing nothing all day.

This answer is merely an absence of something undesired and tells the therapist and client nothing about what will be happening. The therapist will need to continue the conversation.

THERAPIST: What will you be doing instead?

CLIENT: I'll be seeing my friends more often.

THERAPIST: OK, how often do you think you'd be seeing them?

CLIENT: Well, I'd probably be seeing my close friend at least once a week and others less often.

THERAPIST: What would you be doing with your friends when you saw them?

CLIENT: With my close friend I usually go to her house or she comes round to mine and we drink tea and chat and put the world to rights!

THERAPIST: What sort of things do you talk about?

CLIENT: Oh you know, the trouble with men, the price of cigarettes *(laughs)*.

THERAPIST: What is it about being with your friend that you value?

CLIENT: She makes me feel normal and that I'm as good as other people.

THERAPIST: How do you usually arrange to see your friend?

CLIENT: Oh we used to text each other regularly and sort of had a regular arrangement to meet.

THERAPIST: What about your other friends?

And so on.

At the end of this conversation the therapist will look for signs that some of this may be happening already.

THERAPIST: Are there any signs that some of what you've described is happening at the moment?

CLIENT: Well, my friend did text me the other day wondering how I was.

THERAPIST: How did you respond?

CLIENT: I didn't really know what to say so I left it, I but I did feel pleased that she'd thought of me.

The therapist may then encourage the client to identify signs of what would be happening when life was getting better.

> THERAPIST: So, what small sign would let you know that things were getting better?
>
> CLIENT: I might reply to my friend when she texts me or maybe I'll send her a text.
>
> THERAPIST: What difference would that make?
>
> CLIENT: I'd feel like I wasn't all alone and that I was beginning to come out of this depression.

Asking what difference an identified activity would make is a very useful question. It helps clients to remember what is important to them. When people have suffered any sort of mental instability, they can often feel very vulnerable and unsure. Friends, family and health professionals may have given them advice about what to do, which can lead to clients feeling even more incompetent and unsure. There is a sense that asking the above questions is about getting the clients to uncover their own evidence on which they will then base their actions. Sometimes when a therapist asks about a possible difference, the client will say that there would be no difference. This is useful! The client need not then waste their energy and can concentrate on identifying something that *will* make a difference.

These small signs are often things that a therapist would not be able to uncover through formal assessment. Often they are things which could appear trivial and easily overlooked. For example, one client identified being able to complete the crossword of a certain newspaper as a sign of being well. She then used 'being able to do a little bit more of the crossword each week' as a sign of progress. The way this sign was discussed also meant that the client noticed and valued every extra word she was able to get each week, rather than focusing on *still* not being able to complete the crossword.

Another way of starting a conversation about the client's preferred future is to ask what is known as the 'miracle question'.

> – Imagine you go to sleep tonight and while you are sleeping, a miracle happens and the problems that brought you here

today are no longer significant in your life. Because you were sleeping you don't know this miracle happened… so when you wake up, what is the first thing you notice that tells you the miracle has happened?

This question is a powerful way of beginning a conversation about a preferred future. The client is asked to bypass all the problems they are experiencing hence their answer is less constrained by their current experience. It gives the client permission to dream a little. It is important when asking this question to remember this aspect and not be concerned if some answers are unrealistic. We all long for things that are impossible such as being able to lose all that extra weight overnight without having to change our diet or take up exercise. What is useful about answers to this and similar questions is how the client thinks having their answer come true will change their life.

For example, 30 clients might all say in response to this question, 'I would have won the lottery.' The therapist would then ask, 'What difference would this make?' There would probably be 30 different answers all signifying the unique meaning that winning the lottery would make to each client. When we long for things it is usually because it signifies the attainment of something different; there is often a deeper meaning hidden from ourselves. If the therapist does not search for this, they will miss important information. Exploring an unattainable desire often leads to possible actions or solutions that were previously unseen because the focus was solely on the desire.

For example, a playgroup invited one of the authors to run a team building workshop since staff morale was low because they had lost a bid for a new building which they thought would solve their problems. The staff were asked to imagine the 'miracle' playgroup; what it would look like, what would be happening, what they would be doing differently. The staff filled five flipchart pages with ideas. Looking at these they found that of all the identified changes, only one was dependent on a change of venue. They had effectively paralysed themselves by being fixated on something that *symbolised* all the changes they wanted rather than looking at the changes themselves. Clients often become paralysed in the same way, for example when a partner leaves and they see their recovery dependent on getting back with the partner.

Asking the miracle question can therefore lead to a freeing-up of possible solutions by focusing on the minutiae of change. The therapist ensures that the meaning of the desired change is clarified and also that it is, as previously mentioned, expressed in concrete positive terms. When beginning to use the miracle question it is a good idea to contain it through a 'miracle day' from morning to night, eliciting as much detail as possible about each stage. Many solution focused brief therapists always ask the question in this way, while others adapt it to specific situations or timescales. As discussed in the introduction, using the miracle question to gain a detailed picture of daily life in the client's preferred future is a way of getting the client to carry out their own occupational analysis.

Case 1 Janet

Janet, a young woman of 22, was an in-patient having suffered an acute depressive episode following the break-up of her first serious relationship.

THERAPIST: Imagine you go to sleep tonight and while you are sleeping, a miracle happens and life becomes the way you would like it to be. Because you were sleeping you don't know this miracle happened… so when you wake up, what is the first thing you notice that tells you the miracle has happened?

JANET: I wouldn't be feeling sad and depressed all the time.

THERAPIST: What would you be feeling instead?

JANET: I don't know, I suppose I'd be feeling happy.

THERAPIST: How would you know you were feeling happy?

JANET: I wouldn't have this heavy feeling in my stomach.

THERAPIST: So how would your stomach feel?

JANET: *(long pause)*… You know, I think I'd be feeling hungry!

THERAPIST: So what would be the first thing you'd do on this miracle morning?

JANET: Well, I'd get out of bed and make myself some

breakfast.

THERAPIST: What difference would that make?

JANET: It would be different because I have to drag myself out of bed at the moment and don't feel like eating and usually just have some black coffee and a cigarette.

THERAPIST: So what would it be like instead?

JANET: Well, I'd get out of bed sort of looking forward to the day and shower and have a proper breakfast.

THERAPIST: What would you be looking forward to doing?

JANET: Hmm, maybe going to work or doing something nice if it was the weekend.

THERAPIST: Tell me a little bit about how that day would go. How would you know things were different?

JANET: Well, like I said I'd have a proper breakfast. You know at weekends I always used to like a cooked breakfast on a Saturday morning at the local café. I bet they're wondering where I am.

THERAPIST: How else would you know things were different?

JANET: To be honest I'd probably take a little more care of myself.

THERAPIST: Tell me a bit about what you mean by that?

JANET: You know, make sure my clothes were clean and that I'd washed and done my hair. I never used to let my hair get like this. I'd probably put on some make-up.

THERAPIST: What difference would that make?

JANET: I'd feel a lot better about myself, like I mattered.

THERAPIST: So what else would you do if you felt like you mattered?

JANET: I'd go back to college. I was learning hairdressing before I got ill. I've always wanted to be a hairdresser.

THERAPIST: How did you do that – hairdressing?

JANET: Well, you have to learn about how to cut hair,

what products to use, all about how to mix dyes and apply them. I really liked doing braiding and French plaits you know.

THERAPIST: Wow, how did you do that?

JANET: You have to be good with your fingers – you know careful, patient and be good at dividing the hair.

Janet went on to identify other things she would be doing when life was going well. At the end of the conversation the therapist asked:

THERAPIST: So can you see any signs of the miracle happening at the moment?

JANET: You know it's funny but you know Sally on the ward? She knows I was doing hairdressing and she asked if I'd braid her hair - you know she's got that beautiful long hair? I didn't want to do it - I thought I'd probably mess it up – but it did make me feel good that she'd asked me and I'd love to have a go on her hair.

THERAPIST: What else is happening that is a sign that the miracle is beginning to happen?

JANET: Well, yesterday at the social group I realised that I'd enjoyed myself talking to people and hadn't thought about John until I got back to the ward, so maybe I'm beginning to get over all that.

THERAPIST: That's amazing, so how do you think you did that?

JANET: Well, I suppose I was distracted because I was talking to people

THERAPIST: So how did that work?

JANET: I'm not sure, maybe I am getting better at concentrating.

Occupational therapists do not view their clients in isolation. They view humans in a holistic way and consider the wider system of their clients in assessment and intervention. In order to gain a clear picture of their capacity in activities of daily living they consider the relationship between the person, the occupation they are engaging in and the environment in which the occupation is taking place *(Strong et al, 1999)*.

It is this way of thinking that makes it possible for an occupational therapist to see beyond a person's impairments and to adapt occupations or environments to enable occupation. Feelings, thoughts and actions arise from a complex dynamic interplay between internal components and external influences, which could be any kind of input from the colour of a wall to the way someone speaks to them *(Kielhofner, 2002)*. This explains, for example, why clients may perform a task differently at home than in the hospital. It also allows the possibility that changing aspects of the environment, even in a very small way can change behaviour or feelings.

This systemic perspective also occurs within solution focused brief therapy. Building on a conversation about a preferred future, the therapist can include a variety of questions relating to the client's environment and relationships which can help to provide even more meaning or unique markers of a successful outcome.

Questions you could ask would be:
- When the miracle happens what would your spouse (or significant other, family members, close friends etc.) notice that was different?
- What difference would that make?

Case 2 Katherine

Katherine, a youthful 56 year old woman, was referred to the occupational therapist in the community. She had been working for many years as an administrator in a local factory and had the reputation of being extremely hard-working and energetic. She was married and had two adult sons. She was being treated for anxiety and depression following a traumatic incident where her son was falsely accused of a serious offence and was taken from home by armed police. He was subsequently acquitted. After a spell off work she was finding it hard to return because of recurring panic attacks. During the interview Katherine had identified her preferred future as not being at work but being at home reading and gardening. She did not see this as a realistic future but as a 'miracle'.

THERAPIST: So what would your husband notice that was

different when your miracle has happened?

KATHERINE: Well, he'd notice that I was a lot calmer and quieter.

THERAPIST: What difference would that make?

KATHERINE: Actually I think he'd find it rather weird. I'm such an active person always running around doing things for people, seeing friends and so on. I've always done everything at home, made all the decisions, been very concerned about doing everything just so. Since I've been ill I've been doing none of that. I'm not going out and I don't want to see people except my closest friends. That's one of the reasons that he's so worried about me at the moment because I'm not myself.

THERAPIST: So if you got your miracle, your husband would think you were still ill?

KATHERINE: Yes I think so.

THERAPIST: So what would need to be different for you to get your miracle but also not worry your husband.

KATHERINE: I don't know. I've changed so much since [the incident] that I don't think I'll ever be that active person again. I felt so angry that such a thing could happen, I've always tried to be a good person and do things for other people but I feel so tired now. I feel I want to be totally selfish.

THERAPIST: What difference would being selfish make?

KATHERINE: I don't know but I think I deserve to have what I want now and somehow having been forced to stop rushing around has given me time to think and I really enjoy the peacefulness of being at home just doing what I want when I want it. But it's wrong to be selfish isn't it?

THERAPIST: What would your sons say about what you're telling me?

KATHERINE: *(laughs)* They'd say it was about time! They've always said I do too much and should be more selfish.

THERAPIST: OK, so let me ask you again what would need to be different for your husband to accept the new Katherine?

KATHERINE: Well, maybe I need to talk to him more about it, like I've been talking to you. I think he's worried that I'll withdraw from him completely or maybe even leave him, but I still love him just like always. Maybe he needs to know that.

THERAPIST: So how will you know that your husband is OK about some of the changes you'd like to make?

KATHERINE: Well, he'd understand that he'd have to ask me before accepting invitations because I don't want to go out all the time. Really there are only a few people I want to socialise with regularly. Also I think we'd do more things together, just him and me. Simple things like going for a drive and a pub lunch.

THERAPIST: Is talking to your husband about these things a possibility?

KATHERINE: Yes, definitely. He'll find it strange, but I'm sure we could.

Bringing in the systemic view to this conversation allowed Katherine to identify her dilemma. Getting better would mean returning to a life she didn't want any more, but doing more of what she'd discovered she enjoyed could be interpreted by her husband and others as remaining ill. Katherine did talk to her husband, and as she had predicted he did find it strange at first and was very concerned. However, after six months she had left work and started up a flower arranging business which she could do from home. Her relationship with her husband improved as he became used to the new Katherine, and as she grew in confidence, he stopped being concerned.

Exceptions

The power of using a solution focused approach lies in its ability help people to recognise their own strengths and solution-finding capabilities. Rather than focusing on the problem, it is more useful to focus on what will be different when the problem is absent, as one does when asking the miracle question. Equally, rather than focus on the times when things are going wrong, it is more useful to talk about what people are doing or what is happening when a problem is absent, or less of a problem. These times are known as 'exceptions'.

'Exceptions' are a way of talking about times in the client's experience that are not associated or are less associated with their perceived problems or difficulties. People tend to categorise experiences in order to understand or relate to them. For example, most of us will have described a day as a 'bad day' or a 'good day'. People who are depressed will say that they are depressed all of the time and that nothing goes right. If we were to analyse such a day it is unlikely that every moment of a 'bad' day was unhappy, unproductive, unfulfilling or whatever we are categorising as 'bad'. Therefore, it is fair to assume that something will have gone well, or at least not so badly. People tend to be blinded by problems and cannot see beyond them. Focusing the conversation on 'exceptions' (times when the problem isn't happening or is less intense) helps the therapist and client to have a conversation that may alter the client's experience.

Exceptions can take many forms. The therapist will be looking for evidence of the client's skills, competencies, coping strategies and strengths and feeding it back through the conversation or at the end of the session in the form of compliments. The client will begin to recognise and value these qualities that they may have forgotten or not realised that they had. On the part of the client, exceptions can be a particularly rich source of potential solutions or building-blocks towards a solution. They are the expert on their own experience and life and asking exception questions is like mining for information about how, when and where an occupation is carried out that gives clues to achieving the client's preferred future. Every occupational therapist knows that focusing on existing strengths and resources is the most powerful way of enabling people to move from feeling stuck and incapacitated to feeling hopeful and more confident in their abilities. Exception questions provide a focus in conversation to underpin this activity.

Case 1 Janet (continued)

Previously we looked at a conversation between Janet and her therapist who asks if there is a small sign that the miracle is happening. Janet's attention is brought to the fact that she managed not to think about her ex-boyfriend. This could be called searching for an exception, although a therapist would not say this to the client, it is simply a way of getting a therapist to remember to look for these times. The therapist in the example reinforces the exception and conveys the assumption that the client had some control in at least creating some of the conditions necessary for the exception to arise. It is worth exploring the exception and the qualities associated with it because if the client is going to build on existing strengths, this is one place to find them. For example, if we continue the previous conversation on page 18:

> THERAPIST: That's interesting, have you noticed any other signs that your concentration is improving?
>
> JANET: Well, I did manage to read a few pages of a magazine earlier today, I couldn't do more than a few lines when I came in, and I didn't take anything in.
>
> THERAPIST: So if your concentration continues to improve, what difference would that make? What would I see you doing?
>
> JANET: Well, I'd definitely put on make-up every day.
>
> THERAPIST: What else?
>
> JANET: I'd read more, talk more with people, *(laughs)* ... I might even trust myself to have a go at Sally's hair!

Janet's experience of her depression now has some significant chinks in it. She has already demonstrated that she is not 'sad and depressed all the time'. Although the exception is small, she has also identified ways of building on it. What is important is that it is the client who identified her improving concentration as the exception that made the difference. Occupational therapists have often cited 'improving concentration' as a treatment goal and then prescribed activities to improve their client's concentration. Clients may not understand the importance of concentration and may be reluctant to engage in prescribed activities. Janet has identified for herself the functional importance of concentration in terms of her own valued occupations. Her motivation to push herself to improve her concentration is likely to be increased as a result.

A therapist working in a solution focused way is always looking out for exceptions in what a client says, or asks questions to elicit them. Other exception questions might be:

- When are you able to do *X* now? Even in a small way?
- Are there any times when the problem isn't happening or it isn't so severe?
- Can you tell me something about the times when the problem isn't happening?
- What are you doing differently when the problem isn't happening?
- Are there any times when you manage to do (positive behaviour) instead of (negative behaviour)? What is different about those times?

Case 3 Tony

Tony, 50 years old, was referred to a mental health day service following a short admission to an acute in-patient unit. He was under considerable stress regarding his financial situation and his relationship with his wife. As a result of physical difficulties, he had been unable to keep working as a self-employed builder. He seemed to find the first weekly session with the occupational therapist useful and had identified some small goals to work on. However, at the second meeting he had arrived saying that he had had a 'terrible' week.

TONY: I felt really down all week. I just don't see how things at home are going to get any better. I feel so useless not being able to work and support Jenny.

THERAPIST: Sounds like you've had a really hard time. I'm

wondering if anything at all positive happened this week?

TONY: Well, the best thing that happened was my mate Fred took me fishing for the day. I really enjoyed that.

THERAPIST: So what made that day different to the others?

TONY: I felt I had a purpose, I don't do anything at home. My wife does everything and I feel useless. I know how to fish and was able to help my friend. I felt more confident and in control.

The therapist asked Tony more about his fishing skills. During this part of the conversation Tony became animated and smiled a lot. As he spoke it was apparent he was very skilled at fishing. The therapist made use of this exception and asked:

THERAPIST: What needs to happen for you to feel more like this *(confident and in control)* at home?

Tony became thoughtful for a while.

TONY: I'll do more. I'll try and do some cooking for my wife. I did used to cook a couple of times a week. There's no reason I couldn't do that again. I need to get some of my old roles back. Just buying her a bunch of flowers now and again, and little things like that.

If people cannot identify exceptions in the present it can be useful to get clients to think about a time when things were going well or better. This links clients back into thinking about themselves at a time when they were more able to create a satisfactory life and remind them of skills, abilities and attitudes that may have helped them.

   — Can you tell me about a time when you felt in control of your life?

   — What was different when you were able to do these things?

When searching for exceptions a therapist may need to be gently persistent. Although solution focused brief therapy is very client-centred it is not non-directive. By assuming that there must be exceptions, and actively questioning to find them, the client will usually begin to look for them, even if this is after the therapy session. Looking for exceptions is also a useful homework assignment for clients. A typical question might be, 'Notice the times when the problem isn't happening. What are you doing, thinking? Where are you? Who are you with?'

Scales

Questions which ask the client to scale aspects of their experience can be used very effectively in a solution focused way. Typically the therapist will use a 0 to 10 scale where 0 represents the worst and 10 the best. For example:

– On a scale of 0 to 10, where 0 is the worst your life has been and 10 is the best it could be, where are you now?

The answer to this question, if it is above 0, will open up a conversation about what the difference is between where they are now and 0, effectively becoming an exception question. If we remember that we are always asking ourselves whether a question will lead to useful conversation, the answer here can also provide some excellent opportunities for exploring possible futures and exploring what is already contributing to these futures. The therapist can ask the client to describe how life would be at 10. Doing this elicits a 'preferred future', as discussed earlier. If the answer is 0 you should consider asking a 'coping' question such as:

– That sounds like you are at rock bottom, how are you managing to cope?

Coping questions are considered in more depth later in this chapter.

Scale questions are often used after asking the miracle question.

– On a scale of 0 to 10 where 0 is nowhere near the miracle happening and 10 is that it has happened completely, where are you now?

Case 4 James

James, 23, had been detained in hospital for nearly a year under Section 3 of the Mental Health Act (1983). Prior to his admission his behaviour had become bizarre and violent and he reported this was a result of his hearing voices. He had become unable to manage even the simplest tasks of daily living. At the time of the interview he was voluntarily taking a new type of medication which appeared to be keeping him more stable. He had consistently refused to attend occupational therapy and was perceived by the nursing staff as lazy and unco-operative. The therapist used scales to structure the interview and elicit exceptions.

THERAPIST: On a scale of 0 to 10 where 0 is the worst your life has been and 10 is the best it could be, where are you now?

JAMES: Dunno.

The therapist said nothing and waited, maintaining an interested stance. (James actually said 'dunno' before every answer.)

JAMES: About 2.

THERAPIST: That's good, so how come you're at 2 and not at 0?

JAMES: I can go off the ward unescorted now.

THERAPIST: That's a huge difference, how did you manage to do that?

JAMES: Well, the doctor said I could.

THERAPIST: What did the doctor see about you that told her you could be trusted?

JAMES: Well, I suppose something the nurses said.

THERAPIST: Oh right, so what do you think they might have said?

JAMES: That I wasn't getting so mouthy with them maybe.

THERAPIST: OK, so how did you do that?

JAMES: Can't be bothered to any more.

THERAPIST: So can you tell me a little bit about what you think life would be like if you were at a 10 on that scale?

JAMES: Well, I wouldn't be in here for a start! I'd have my own flat and a job and a girlfriend.

THERAPIST: That sounds good, what do you think you'd be doing during the day?

JAMES: Get up, have some tea and a fag, play a bit of guitar, watch TV…

THERAPIST: What about the job?

JAMES: Oh yeah, not sure, nothing too demanding *(laughs)*.

THERAPIST: *(laughs)* Well, there are some jobs like that. What else would you be doing when you are living in your own flat?

JAMES: I guess I'd have to do a bit of housework or else I'd have to be rich and get a maid *(laughs)*.

THERAPIST: What sort of housework do you see yourself doing?

JAMES: Bit of cleaning, hoover now and then, cook meals.

THERAPIST: What sort of meals will you cook?

JAMES: Curries, I love curries but I don't know how to make them.

THERAPIST: OK, so can you tell me, if I come and see you next week and you tell me you're at 2½, what will be different? What will have happened?

JAMES: 2½? Can you cook curries? Can you teach me how to cook a curry? You've got a kitchen down there *(the occupational therapy department)*, you do cooking with people.

Following this conversation, James attended the occupational therapy department for the first time since admission and made his first of many curries. He also asked for his guitar to be brought into the hospital and began to play it regularly.

People with disrupted thought patterns respond well to questions using scales. It may be that they provide a structure that aids their engaging with progress. Without prompting, James framed all his subsequent conversations with the occupational therapist around scales.

Exceptions can also be used indirectly on behalf of the client. Due to his previous disruptive behaviour on the ward, James had a poor reputation among the nursing staff. Since they had influence on the picture of James' progress presented in ward rounds, the occupational therapist asked the nursing staff to help her by noticing the times when James engaged in purposeful and appropriate behaviours on the ward. This began to break down the nurses' perception of James as lazy and doing nothing all day. They also noticed that he was making an effort to be more polite and co-operative, although neither the therapist nor client had identified that as a goal.

Problem-Free Talk

Problem-free talk will normally occur at the beginning of an interview and will contribute to forming a rapport. It refers to questions that bear no relation to the presenting problem and usually focuses on the client's interests and skills. In this sense it is a type of exception-based conversation.

By the time you see a client, it is likely that they will have already discussed their problems at length with a variety of people; friends, family, GP, social workers, health professionals. They may have built up a fairly clear picture of the problem and also begun to have some theories about why or how it arose. They may also have been given varied advice on how best to deal with their problem. In order to justify their need for help, they will have had to identify closely with the problem, some may even feel that they *are* the problem. Many will have been given a diagnostic label which is often expressed in personal terms, for example, 'I am a schizophrenic.'

To begin the process of separating the person from the problem, talking to them in a problem-free manner allows the client to refocus on areas of themselves and their lives which have receded into the background. It also enables the therapist to gain information into the client's skills and qualities that could be useful in constructing solutions. It is not uncommon for therapists to begin constructing solutions with the client even at this early stage of the interview.

While talking to the client, it is useful for the therapist to practice 'constructive listening'. This means that during the conversation the therapist is looking for evidence of what the client does well and what their skills and resources are. These are the unique tools the client will use to overcome their difficulties.

Some examples for introducing problem-free talk might be:

– It would be helpful for me to know something about you aside from whatever brought you here today, for example your interests or hobbies.

- Can you tell me a little about the things you enjoy doing?
- Can you tell me a little about the things you are good at?

Case 5 Sally

Sally, 46, was referred to the community mental health occupational therapist for help in coping with her anxiety. She had a history of amphetamine abuse and had a conviction for dealing cannabis. She had a 9 year old son who was on the 'at risk' register of Social Services and she was very concerned that she would lose him.

THERAPIST: It would be helpful for me to know something about you aside from whatever brought you here today, for example your interests or hobbies.

SALLY: Well, my main interests are looking after my son and my animals.

THERAPIST: What sort of animals do you have?

SALLY: I have four cockatiels and three rabbits, a cockatoo and a gecko.

THERAPIST: Wow! That's quite a lot of animals.

SALLY: Yeah, they're beautiful, I've had them for years. Two of the cockatiels are the babies of the other two. I got the gecko for a fiver at a car-boot fair. I don't think it had been treated right and I took him to the vet. He said he wouldn't live but that's a year ago and he's fine. The vet said he'd never seen such a healthy one outside of a zoo.

THERAPIST: That's quite an achievement, does your son help look after the animals?

SALLY: No, he just likes to play with the rabbits but I do it all.

This is very important information. Caring for animals requires commitment and discipline.

THERAPIST: So you feed them every day and clean out their cages?

SALLY: Yes.

THERAPIST: How do you do that?

SALLY: Well, you just do it don't you?

THERAPIST: Do you get up in the morning to do it?

SALLY: Oh yes, of course.

THERAPIST: Even after you've had a late night and been partying?

SALLY: Yes, of course I do, otherwise they'd wonder what was going on. They need to be fed at the right time and all that, you got to do that with animals.

THERAPIST: Well, I think that's pretty impressive. It takes a lot of discipline and self-will to do that doesn't it?

SALLY: I never thought of it like that before. I suppose it does.

THERAPIST: How about your son, do you look after him like you do the animals?

SALLY: Oh yeah! Better. He's always got a clean pair of socks to put on every day, he's always at school on time. He eats well, I'd do anything for him. I'm a good mum you know, there's a lot worse on this estate, but just because I was a bit stupid with the blow and all that…

Sally at this point is more relaxed and co-operative with the therapist. She feels that the therapist is 'The first person to understand me and not judge me'. As Sally feels negatively judged by the social workers she has become unco-operative with their requests. The therapist can now build on Sally's strengths as follows:

THERAPIST: OK, so what are the social workers not seeing about the way you care for your son that causes them to worry?

SALLY: They don't see that even though I do silly things, I make sure my son's OK.

THERAPIST: How would they know that your son's OK?

SALLY: They could ask the school about him, they can't understand why he's at risk. They said they wished more parents were like me.

THERAPIST: Right, and what could you do that would help them

SALLY: see the caring mother that you are?

SALLY: I don't think there's much I can do.

THERAPIST: Well, we've already established that you are capable of discipline and self-will and that that's an important part of being able to care, so how could they see that more clearly?

SALLY: Well, I suppose I could turn up on time to appointments and be a bit more polite to them.

THERAPIST: That'd be a good start, what else?

SALLY: Maybe I could get the school to write a letter or something.

THERAPIST: That's a good idea, what else?

SALLY: Maybe I could invite them to meet with me at the house and they could see that it was clean and all that.

Using the miracle question discussed earlier, the therapist went on from here to discuss how Sally saw her ideal future.

Pre-Session Change

Once people make the decision to ask for help, or when they have been referred, they often begin to make changes even before the first appointment. At the very least they begin to think about what they might hope to get from seeing you. Eliciting these changes is an excellent way of empowering your client since they can all be attributed to their own efforts. In this, as in all parts of a solution focused conversation, the therapist is looking for strengths and resources that can be built on. Questions focusing on pre-session change are a type of exception question.

Examples of questions could be:

– Since making the appointment to see me today have you thought about how seeing me could be helpful? What is your best hope?

– Since making the appointment, have you noticed any changes in your situation for the better? How did you do that?

    – Since being in hospital have you had noticed any
       improvement? How have you done that?

As has already been seen, after asking preferred future questions you could ask:

    – Have you seen any signs that the miracle is already starting to
       happen? What difference has that made? How did you do that?

In order to encourage awareness of pre-session changes, some therapists make use of a pre-appointment question sheet sent with the invitation for an interview, which the client brings to the first meeting. Alternatively you can make suggestions in the letter, such as 'Before you come to the meeting, it would be helpful if you could notice any positive changes, however small, that are happening already so that we can discuss them.'

Coping Questions

Coping questions are also a type of exception question. Sometimes clients are unable to respond usefully to questions that focus on the future. This may be because they are too distressed or their situation seems so difficult and complicated. For a variety of reasons some clients end up having a long admission, and focusing on the future can be hard, especially if their life prior to admission was chaotic or they have lost a job or home while in hospital. At times, clients' problems are so overwhelming they are unable to identify or describe times when the problem is not happening or happening less. In these situations it is important not to move too swiftly into solutions or the client may feel the therapist did not understand them or the gravity of their situation. In order to both listen respectfully and begin to focus on what the client is doing well already, it is better to ask questions that focus on how the client is coping. These enable the therapist and client to start agreeing on what the client is doing that is useful and begin to shift the client's perception of the situation away from passivity and helplessness.

Sometimes individuals take considerable time in discussing their past, they need to feel 'heard' and have their experiences acknowledged by a professional. This process may need to happen before any goal-setting is discussed.

Therapists, in general, are keen to move on to setting goals and 'moving forward' and can rush clients or become frustrated by those who seem to want to continue complaining about their situation despite the best efforts of the therapist. It is natural to want the client's life to improve. However, a lesson from practice which was shared with the authors provides a reminder of the importance of moving at the client's pace.

Case 6 Ellen

Ellen, a middle-aged woman, had been attending a community mental health centre for about six years. A number of different professionals had been involved in her care, all of whom reported her to be a difficult person to work with and somebody who did not want to make any changes to her life. She was often described as obstructive, critical of services and very tiring to engage with. Ellen would often describe the professionals she encountered over the years as inexperienced, uninterested, pushy and uncaring. Relationships were breaking down and a new approach was clearly needed to resolve this unsatisfactory situation.

Ellen was suffering from low mood and reduced energy levels and often complained of finding it hard to leave the house. She had a large family many of whom suffered from physical and mental health difficulties, as well as children and grandchildren with learning and behavioural problems. She was clearly much relied on and an important family member.

A colleague who had recently undertaken some basic training in solution focused practice decided that he would try and adopt a different approach with Ellen. Over seven one-hour sessions he took the time to listen to Ellen and her views regarding her difficulties and life experiences. He asked questions and acknowledged her distress. He asked how she coped with difficult family relationships and was able to identify that she was a very strong woman who could offer valuable support to a number of people and that she did not really want things to be any different. She set one goal, which was to take some time every day to do something for herself in order to keep her energy levels up and stay strong for her family.

At the end of the seven sessions, Ellen stated that she had never felt listened to before and had never had anyone reflect with her about how difficult her life had been and indeed still was. She announced that she no longer needed to attend the day service and agreed to be discharged from the mental health team as she felt there was no further input that she required. It seems incredible that more had been achieved in seven hours than had been over the previous six years. When using solution focused practice it is common to be surprised and humbled by clients.

It is worth remembering, however, that 'coping' is understood differently by different people. Many clients think that to cope means to be able to act as if nothing had happened in the face of real trauma. It can be useful to explore this.

Examples of coping questions might be:

- It sounds like you are having a hard time. What are you doing to cope?
- What are you doing to help you get through the day?
- How do you cope day to day?
- What keeps you a tiny bit hopeful that things could change?
- Can you tell me about a time when you were able to cope well? How did you do that? Could you do some of those things now?
- If you thought you were coping well with things what would you be doing?

Case 7 Karen

Karen, a 48 year old nurse, was seen by the community occupational therapist. Her only child, a son, had been killed abroad in an accident which had destroyed his body. In addition, the authorities had not prosecuted the company responsible so Karen felt there had been no justice. Since the bereavement she had completely withdrawn from life and spent her days at home alone. She was at risk of losing her job.

> THERAPIST: I cannot imagine how difficult life must be for you now. How do you cope?
>
> KAREN: I don't think I cope at all.

THERAPIST: What are you doing to help you get through the day?

KAREN: Most of the time I am just going through the motions – you know, getting up, getting dressed, having some food – when I can be bothered to do those things, sometimes I don't get up at all.

THERAPIST: When you 'go through the motions', how do you do that?

KAREN: I just force myself, I tell myself I have to do it, that I can't just do nothing.

THERAPIST: Ok, so some days you listen to yourself and do what you're told – what's different about those times?

KAREN: Hmm, I'm not sure, I think on those days I imagine my son and how unhappy he'd be to see me like this, but then most of the time I think well he's dead so he's not going to see me so what's the point?

THERAPIST: So when you imagine your son being able to see you and still care about you you're able to do some basic things to care for yourself?

KAREN: Yes.

THERAPIST: When are you able to hold on to that image of your son still caring about you and you don't give in to the negative feelings?

KAREN: I don't know.

THERAPIST: Do you think you could try to notice that for me before we meet again?

At the next session Karen told the therapist that she realised she was more able to hold on to the image of her son still caring about her when she stopped spending time bed staring at pictures of her son in the morning. The occupational therapist worked out a daily routine with Karen (this had been negotiated at a different part of the session) to re-establish a more normal daily pattern. Karen worked out a time of day that she was able to look at her son's photos without it causing so much distress and this was included in her daily routine. Eventually Karen felt able to cope with seeing a bereavement counsellor.

Giving Compliments/Positive Feedback

Highlighting people's strengths and resources through feedback and encouragement is recognised by occupational therapists as important in helping to form a rapport and to increase the client's motivation and sense of efficacy. In solution focused brief therapy it is also considered an important part of the conversation. Occupational therapists tend to do this as they go along, giving words of praise and encouragement throughout contact with a client, either individually or in a group. It is more usual in the solution focused context to formulate verbal feedback based on the therapist's observations of the client's strengths, abilities and qualities, and to share this with the client at the end of a session.

Although during a solution focused brief therapy session, the therapist will give words of encouragement and express when they are impressed or interested by something the client has said or done during the conversation, giving positive feedback at the end of the session could be considered a summing up of all that the therapist has learned. It is useful to create a break between the end of the conversation or interview and the time when the feedback is given. The therapist could say:

"I am going to take a little time and think about all we've discussed so I can give you some feedback."

Some therapists like to leave the room for a few minutes to do this, others spend some time in front of the client jotting down notes while others may simply take time to reflect by looking through their session notes. During this time the therapist will be looking for:

– Evidence of strengths
– Evidence of qualities
– Evidence of abilities
– Evidence of exception behaviour

This evidence may not be immediately obvious but the more skilled the therapist is in formulating positive feedback the more they can deduce strengths from even a simple conversation. In certain settings, this more formal way of giving feedback can be incorporated into an occupational therapy interview.

Creating a break between the interview and the feedback also changes the dynamic between the therapist and client. There will be an expectation that the client is listening to the therapist and that the time for giving the therapist information is now over. Clients, for the most part, are very interested in what the therapist has to say and they want to know what the therapist was thinking about. Most of the time they are expecting to be told what their problems are and how they arose or what they have done wrong. They are often surprised and sometimes moved by what they hear. If the feedback is given at the end of the session, this is the last thing the clients hear and it is what they take away with them. An end of session feedback may sound like this:

Case 8 Gary

Gary, 32, married with two small children, suffered with chronic pain due to an inflammatory disease. He had to give up work and became depressed. He had almost completely withdrawn from family life, and since he relied on his wife to do everything at home, she was unable to work and they had little money. Gary had been referred by his GP because of concerns about his mental state and also because it was thought that Gary was far more disabled than his condition warranted. After an initial interview based around the Solution Focused Measure of Occupational Function the following feedback was given.

"Thank you for allowing me to come and see you today and for spending time talking to me. From what you have told me it sounds like you have been having a really difficult time over the last few years trying to cope with a frightening condition. I was impressed how you were willing to try out all the different treatments offered and that despite the disappointment of nothing working so far, you are still willing to see the specialist in January. From what you've told me it's obvious that you care deeply about your family as you are concerned that your condition has stopped you from contributing to the family like you used to do. Your wife is very supportive of you, which suggests to me that you still have qualities that you contribute to the relationship even if you can't see that at the moment. You showed self-awareness when you realised that you were in danger of becoming addicted to morphine and it must have taken a lot of determination to stop using it for pain relief. You have shown that you can learn a new skill by learning to use a computer. You were telling me about your job as a carpenter before you became ill and it sounds like you are a very organised person who plans carefully before you start something to ensure that the job is done properly and that doing something properly is a matter of pride for you."

At the next session two weeks later, Gary told the therapist that he had, for the first time, discussed the possibility with his wife that he would never recover fully from his condition and his fears that she would leave him. He had been amazed to discover that the reasons she loved him were nothing to do with his role as a breadwinner. He said that he had prepared a plan for slowly getting back into family life so his wife could work and that in the long-term he was considering retraining in a computer-based career. He worked collaboratively with the occupational therapist over the next six months on a graded programme to develop a balanced domestic routine and was able to appropriately use aids provided by the community physical occupational therapist whom he had previously refused to see.

This chapter has provided a very brief overview of solution focused brief therapy and examples of how it has been incorporated into occupational therapy practice. The principles of solution focused working are very simple but in practice it is often hard to move away from being problem focused. However, with time and commitment to developing a solution focus, the reward of seeing clients flourish and take control of their lives provides confidence in the approach. Occupational therapists are already familiar with the power of believing in a client's potential for change. Solution focused working will enhance this aspect of their practice.

The next chapter introduces a semi-structured interview tool that was developed to bring a solution focus to a typical occupational therapy activity – the initial interview. Understanding the principles of solution focused brief therapy described in this chapter will help the reader make sense of the thinking behind the Solution Focused Measure of Occupational Function.

CHAPTER TWO

THE SOLUTION FOCUSED MEASURE OF OCCUPATIONAL FUNCTION

Lucie Duncan, Sarah Mousley and Rayya Ghul

In Chapter One we saw how solution focused questioning works in situations familiar to occupational therapists working within mental health services. In this and subsequent chapters we will introduce readers to some practical ideas that have been developed to integrate solution focused working more directly into parts of the occupational therapy process.

Assessment is the first stage of the occupational therapy process and is recognised as a core skill of occupational therapy. This stage is generally seen as part of a linear process moving from assessment to treatment planning, intervention and then evaluation. The focus of any assessment in occupational therapy is ultimately to provide information regarding the factors that contribute to the person's ability to live as independent a life as possible. This is true even if it is only a specific area of function that is being assessed at the time. The occupational therapist will consider the information gained from the assessment in terms of how it affects the person's daily life function. When thinking about how solution focused working could be incorporated into occupational therapy assessment it seemed important to retain this focus, and this has influenced the development of many of the ideas presented here.

Occupational therapy assessment is carried out in a wide variety of ways including observation, interview, structured and semi-structured tools. The assessment process is often very complex to ensure all areas of function and the environment are considered. Using a solution focused approach allows the expertise and experience of the client to become a central tool in this process, cutting down time and effort as client and therapist collaborate on identifying a detailed picture of desired change. This collaboration brings together the client's knowledge of their own life, with the occupational therapist's understanding of the building-blocks of successful independent living. An added bonus of using a solution focused approach is that while the occupational therapist might regard the stage as 'assessment', the client may experience an immediate therapeutic benefit and begin to collaborate on setting goals. This is one of the reasons that this form of working produces 'brief' interventions. Positive change can occur at any time as a result of any part of a solution focused conversation.

Occupational therapists' expertise is the understanding and analysis of daily life. They therefore have enormous faith in the power of simply engaging more successfully in daily life, thereby bringing increased health and well-being. Part of this growing knowledge-base is an increased understanding of occupation as being more than simply a set of activities carried out by a person. New definitions have emerged which suggest that a distinction can be drawn between the real life experience of daily living tasks and the same tasks carried out purely as an exercise in skill, separate from everyday life *(Pierce, 2001b, Wilcock, 1998)*. The former can be described as an 'occupation' and the latter as an 'activity' *(Pierce, 2001a)*. Occupation, as a description of real life, is characterised as existing only in relation to the person who is carrying it out, while activities are merely the way we categorise a set of actions. In other words, making a cup of tea in an occupational therapy kitchen is an activity whereas making a cup of tea just the way you like it in your own kitchen at home is an occupation.

So why is this distinction important? These ideas are a little hard to grasp when encountered for the first time but it is worth spending some time considering the implications of thinking in this way. As occupational therapists use daily life tasks as interventions it is important to be clear how and why we are doing so. If you think of occupations as being brought alive by the person doing them you begin to see that just as in any relationship, there develops an element of familiarity and even comfort in the way we do things. For example, this could be making tea in a pot rather than a mug; using a tea cup instead of a mug; being able to reach for the teabags even when half asleep because you know your kitchen so well; recognising the sound of your kettle; having tea at the same time every day. These types of experience all add up to a sense of 'rightness' about what we are doing. This could be described as an 'occupational meaning'; it is why people do things the way they do and also why they carry on doing them. It is this occupational meaning that is lost when people go into a hospital or residential home and why skills are often neglected or not carried out at all.

An occupational therapist who understands these differences will be more likely to want to spend time finding out which occupations people value and how and why they are carried out in certain ways. However, this can be very time consuming. Becoming more solution focused in interviews provides an easier way to link into people's occupational meanings. Asking how people will *know* that life is going well, or versions of that question, elicits a wide range of responses which may include a detailed daily routine, subjective experiences and aspects of the environment, all of which could take many assessments to uncover. To an occupational therapist this provides a rich source of information that can be used in collaborating with clients to develop solutions that are more likely to work, instead of 'prescribing' activities and blaming the client for not co-operating.

Occupational therapists might work 'hands on' accompanying clients to their homes and into the community so desired changes can be initiated in a practical way. For example, a wish to dress differently may result in a shopping trip with a client who is not yet confident on their own. Occupational therapists also visit clients in their homes and workplaces where they can observe occupational performance. Adopting a solution focused approach would mean that occupational therapists would be looking for exceptions, the times when the client was doing something well, showing aptitude, doing part of whatever behaviour constituted a desired change, noticing and amplifying these through positive feedback and compliments. Being able to meet a client in their own environment is an advantage that occupational therapists have over office-based therapists from other professions.

Chapter One provided some ideas of how interviews can become more solution focused by asking about small signs of change, exceptions and strengths and resources. Observation focuses on more than people's deficits and can pick up abilities, skills, exceptions and successes. However, thinking about applying a solution focus to using assessment tools led to the decision to develop our own tool which eventually became the Solution Focused Measure of Occupational Function. The tool and its use will form the main content of the rest of this chapter.

The Solution Focused Measure of Occupational Function

The Solution Focused Measure of Occupational Function is a semi-structured interview tool which encourages collaboration between client and therapist. The Measure reflects the domains of concern of occupational therapy, such as those described by the Canadian Model of Occupational Performance (CAOT, 2004): Productivity, Self-Care and Leisure.

The structure is designed to allow the client to demonstrate their unique understanding and expertise within each area. Because it is semi-structured, therapists can ask supplementary solution focused questions to draw out the occupational meanings within each aspect. This will link in to the dynamic and systemic aspects of occupation described within the Model of Human Occupation *(Kielhofner, 2002)* as volition (the drivers of occupation) and habituation (the patterns of occupation). It is assumed that readers will have at least passing knowledge of these models.

The Measure includes a number of questions that focus on general mental health and well-being. However, these questions also have a functional aspect which is enhanced by solution focused questioning since this focuses on what the client will be *doing* differently. This is discussed more thoroughly in the next section, 'Exploring the detail of everyday life'. These areas are particularly important when working with people suffering from conditions which are slow to show improvement in performing task-based activities or higher cognitive functions but whose general mental health may improve or stabilise as a result of occupational therapy intervention. On the other hand, responses to questions focusing on function may show improvement in clients whose psychological symptoms are not necessarily reduced. Such clients are often those characterised as having 'severe and enduring' mental health problems. Although this is a better term than the previously used 'chronic', it is worth remembering that it is still a label which can limit both progress and the perception of progress in the mind of the clinician as well as the client. It is also not helpful if one is promoting recovery from mental distress. Occupational therapists have traditionally focused on ability rather than disability and using the Measure can be seen as part of this tradition. Such information from the Measure can be used as evidence of a client's ability, which can then be shared with other team members.

When participating in a conversation based on the Measure, the client is asked to rate themselves in relation to each statement on a four point scale of 'not at all', 'sometimes', 'mostly' and 'definitely'. This scale can be thought of as corresponding to the use of number scaling whereby 'not at all' would be 0 and 'definitely' would be 10. The choice of only four points on the scale is deliberate, removing the possibility of a middle point which often serves as an easy option on a questionnaire. It also means that all points above 'not at all' must contain some evidence of function, or in solution focused terms, an 'exception'. To promote the solution focus the statements are framed as positive statements rather than statements of dysfunction, so clients rate themselves on what they *can* do. This simple reversal of the way many self-rated assessments are usually designed gives the client the chance to view even tiny achievements as significant and as a stepping-stone to improvement.

The first draft of the Measure was designed by Lucie Duncan and Sarah Mousley and has subsequently been modified by all three authors. Changes were also made as a result of comments from individuals using the Measure. The similarity to other measures such as the Solution Focused Recovery Scale for Abuse Survivors *(Dolan, 1988, 1993, Dolan & Johnson, 1995)* and the Solution Focused Measure of Health *(Webster & Johnson, 1997)* is wholly coincidental but recognised by Rayya Ghul when shown the first draft.

'Measure' is a more useful term for therapist and client because it retains a certain objectivity, as opposed to 'assessment' which necessitates judgement and is generally carried out by one person on another. A 'measure' provides information that the occupational therapist and client can look at together and discuss collaboratively and from which the occupational therapist can engage in clinical reasoning. Occupational therapists may end up using the information gathered by the Measure as part of an assessment, but it is intended primarily as a conversation tool to enhance therapeutic collaboration.

The occupational therapist using the Measure does not need to understand solution focused brief therapy in order to use it. However, it is preferable to have some familiarity with the solution focused questions as described in Chapter One. This supports the use of the Measure as a semi-structured interview tool and the intention that participating in the interview will have a therapeutic benefit in itself. With this in mind, it is important to retain the use of the Measure for face to face contact only and giving the client the Measure to fill out on their own is strongly discouraged. This is because the opportunity to discuss the meaning of the client's responses and to build on strengths is lost. The Measure loses its occupational focus and becomes merely a tick list of activities and skills.

It is up to the occupational therapist when to use the Measure. The authors' preference is to use it during the first formal meeting with a client. We say this because, for example, in an in-patient unit the occupational therapist may have chatted informally to a client prior to seeing them for interview. In an in-patient setting it is more useful to use the Measure when a client's more acute symptoms have settled down. After participating in an interview using the Measure, the information gained may indicate the need for more traditional assessments, such as a specific memory assessment or a home visit to assess daily living skills. This might arise for instance if a client rates themselves as having no problems with self-care when their presentation suggests otherwise.

The Measure also includes a Summary and Progress Sheet to record the responses and provide a baseline which can be reviewed regularly. There are spaces for recording notes after each question. A copy of the Measure without notes is included and can be given to the client as their own record.

Feedback from occupational therapists using the Measure suggest that the occupational performance areas named on the Summary and Progress sheets provide a good framework for structuring reports which clearly reflect occupational therapy practice. The name of each area can be used as a heading in the report and it is easy to write up the information gained. For example:

Environment

Miss B lives alone in a warden-controlled flat. She reports that she is happy with her environment most of the time but finds it hard to use her cooker. Through discussion she identified that having some clearer instructions on how to use and adjust the controls would improve her confidence to cook a wider range of foods.

Mobility

Miss B rarely goes out and feels isolated and dependent on others for her shopping and other needs. She would like to become more confident in going out on her own and would like to learn to use the bus which takes residents on her estate to the supermarket. She saw this as a priority to work on with the occupational therapist and said that if she were able to do this she could become more interested in cooking and improve her diet and therefore her health. She thought this could eventually lead to using other forms of public transport and being able to visit friends, shop for clothes and possibly do some voluntary work.

Writing a report which follows areas covered by the Measure will naturally follow the direction set by the client while retaining an occupational focus. The report will then enable other disciplines and agencies to see clearly where the focus of assessment and/or intervention has been. This promotes a more effective liaison and increases the profile of occupational therapy. The report will also be easily understood by the client, who should receive a copy of it.

When the Measure is used throughout an occupational therapy service it forms a link between different settings such as an acute in-patient unit and the community. Progress that has begun during an admission can be continued on discharge. The community occupational therapist can build on the Measure using the Summary and Progress sheet and the details in a report. Similarly, if a community client is admitted to hospital, the ward-based occupational therapist will be able to discuss past goals and achievements and investigate with the client what may have stopped working and what needs to happen in order for them to return home. In either case, the occupational therapist may ask some or all of the questions again in order to gain a clear picture of present difficulties. The Measure will be familiar to the client and they should experience a sense of continuity.

The following pages may be photocopied or downloaded from http://www.btpress.co.uk/cpf – if photocopied, they are designed to be scaled up from A5 to A4 (scaled up to 141% of their original size).

The Solution Focused Measure of Occupational Function

Name: .... DOB: .... Date: ....

1 | **I am able to talk to people** | Definitely | Mostly | Sometimes | Not at all

2 | **I have satisfying relationships** | Definitely | Mostly | Sometimes | Not at all

3 | **I have confidence in myself** | Definitely | Mostly | Sometimes | Not at all

4 | **I can stand up for myself (be reasonably assertive)** | Definitely | Mostly | Sometimes | Not at all

5 | **I am able to make decisions when I need to** | Definitely | Mostly | Sometimes | Not at all

6 | **I am satisfied with my home environment** | Definitely | Mostly | Sometimes | Not at all

7 | **I can take care of myself (e.g. personal hygiene tasks)** | Definitely | Mostly | Sometimes | Not at all

Client's signature: .... Therapist's signature: ....

The Solution Focused Measure of Occupational Function

Name: .... DOB: .... Date: ....

8 I am able to take care of the place where I live, including laundry, shopping and cooking

Definitely   Mostly   Sometimes   Not at all

9 I can manage my finances

Definitely   Mostly   Sometimes   Not at all

10 I can organise my week in a way that works for me/ satisfies me

Definitely   Mostly   Sometimes   Not at all

11 I can get to where I want and need to go

Definitely   Mostly   Sometimes   Not at all

12 I am able to calm myself when needed

Definitely   Mostly   Sometimes   Not at all

13 I have positive ways of coping with angry feelings

Definitely   Mostly   Sometimes   Not at all

14 I am able to achieve what I set out to do

Definitely   Mostly   Sometimes   Not at all

15 I am able to maintain my concentration and attention on activities that are important to me

Definitely   Mostly   Sometimes   Not at all

Client's signature: .... Therapist's signature: ....

The Solution Focused Measure of Occupational Function

Name: .... DOB: .... Date: ....

16 I am able to solve problems as they arise — Definitely — Mostly — Sometimes — Not at all

17 I can get so involved in a project or activity that I can forget about my discomfort/problems — Definitely — Mostly — Sometimes — Not at all

18 I am able to contribute to meeting the needs of my family (if applicable) — Definitely — Mostly — Sometimes — Not at all

19 I am able to function adequately at work (if applicable) — Definitely — Mostly — Sometimes — Not at all

20 I would like to be able to work/retrain — Definitely — Mostly — Sometimes — Not at all

21 I can enjoy myself — Definitely — Mostly — Sometimes — Not at all

22 I take regular exercise — Definitely — Mostly — Sometimes — Not at all

23 I get enough rest and sleep — Definitely — Mostly — Sometimes — Not at all

Client's signature:.. Therapist's signature:....................................

Name: .... DOB: .... Date: ....

24 **I have people who understand and support me**   Definitely   Mostly   Sometimes   Not at all

....
....
....
....

25 **I can make positive goals for the future**   Definitely   Mostly   Sometimes   Not at all

....
....
....
....

Supplementary question (optional)

Which are the main areas from the above list you would most like to see change happening? Detail desired changes.

....
....
....
....
....
....
....
....
....
....
....
....
....

What small steps can you take towards making this happen?

....
....
....
....
....
....
....
....
....
....
....
....
....

Client's signature: .... Therapist's signature: ....

The Solution Focused Measure of Occupational Function
Summary and progress sheet

Name: .... DOB: .... Date: ....

	Treatment area	Baseline Date:				Review Date:				Review Date:				Achieved Date:	
1	Communication	D	M	S	N	D	M	S	N	D	M	S	N	Y	N
2	Relationships	D	M	S	N	D	M	S	N	D	M	S	N	Y	N
3	Confidence	D	M	S	N	D	M	S	N	D	M	S	N	Y	N
4	Assertiveness	D	M	S	N	D	M	S	N	D	M	S	N	Y	N
5	Decision Making	D	M	S	N	D	M	S	N	D	M	S	N	Y	N
6	Home Environment	D	M	S	N	D	M	S	N	D	M	S	N	Y	N
7	Domestic ADL	D	M	S	N	D	M	S	N	D	M	S	N	Y	N
8	Personal ADL	D	M	S	N	D	M	S	N	D	M	S	N	Y	N
9	Budgeting	D	M	S	N	D	M	S	N	D	M	S	N	Y	N
10	Organisation/routine	D	M	S	N	D	M	S	N	D	M	S	N	Y	N
11	Mobility	D	M	S	N	D	M	S	N	D	M	S	N	Y	N
12	Anxiety Management	D	M	S	N	D	M	S	N	D	M	S	N	Y	N
13	Anger Management	D	M	S	N	D	M	S	N	D	M	S	N	Y	N
14	Positive Focus	D	M	S	N	D	M	S	N	D	M	S	N	Y	N
15	Concentration/Attention	D	M	S	N	D	M	S	N	D	M	S	N	Y	N
16	Problem solving	D	M	S	N	D	M	S	N	D	M	S	N	Y	N
17	Activity engagement	D	M	S	N	D	M	S	N	D	M	S	N	Y	N
18	Family Needs	D	M	S	N	D	M	S	N	D	M	S	N	Y	N
19	Work skills	D	M	S	N	D	M	S	N	D	M	S	N	Y	N
20	Work/Training	D	M	S	N	D	M	S	N	D	M	S	N	Y	N
21	Enjoyment	D	M	S	N	D	M	S	N	D	M	S	N	Y	N
22	Exercise	D	M	S	N	D	M	S	N	D	M	S	N	Y	N
23	Rest/sleep	D	M	S	N	D	M	S	N	D	M	S	N	Y	N
24	Support networks	D	M	S	N	D	M	S	N	D	M	S	N	Y	N
25	Hopefulness	D	M	S	N	D	M	S	N	D	M	S	N	Y	N

D - Definitely M - Mostly S - Sometimes N - Not at all

Client's signature:.. Therapist's signature:..

The Solution Focused Measure of Occupational Function

Name: .... DOB: .... Date: ....

1	I am able to talk to people	Definitely	Mostly	Sometimes	Not at all
2	I have satisfying relationships	Definitely	Mostly	Sometimes	Not at all
3	I have confidence in myself	Definitely	Mostly	Sometimes	Not at all
4	I can stand up for myself (be reasonably assertive)	Definitely	Mostly	Sometimes	Not at all
5	I am able to make decisions when I need to	Definitely	Mostly	Sometimes	Not at all
6	I am satisfied with my home environment	Definitely	Mostly	Sometimes	Not at all
7	I can take care of myself (e.g. personal hygiene tasks)	Definitely	Mostly	Sometimes	Not at all
8	I am able to take care of the place where I live, including laundry, shopping and cooking	Definitely	Mostly	Sometimes	Not at all
9	I can manage my finances	Definitely	Mostly	Sometimes	Not at all
10	I can organise my week in a way that works for me/ satisfies me	Definitely	Mostly	Sometimes	Not at all
11	I can get to where I want and need to go	Definitely	Mostly	Sometimes	Not at all
12	I am able to calm myself when needed	Definitely	Mostly	Sometimes	Not at all
13	I have positive ways of coping with angry feelings	Definitely	Mostly	Sometimes	Not at all
14	I am able to achieve what I set out to do	Definitely	Mostly	Sometimes	Not at all
15	I am able to maintain my concentration and attention on activities that are important to me	Definitely	Mostly	Sometimes	Not at all
16	I am able to solve problems as they arise	Definitely	Mostly	Sometimes	Not at all
17	I can get so involved in a project or activity that I can forget about my discomfort/problems	Definitely	Mostly	Sometimes	Not at all
18	I am able to contribute to meeting the needs of my family (if applicable)	Definitely	Mostly	Sometimes	Not at all
19	I am able to function adequately at work (if applicable)	Definitely	Mostly	Sometimes	Not at all
20	I would like to be able to work/retrain	Definitely	Mostly	Sometimes	Not at all
21	I can enjoy myself	Definitely	Mostly	Sometimes	Not at all
22	I take regular exercise	Definitely	Mostly	Sometimes	Not at all
23	I get enough rest and sleep	Definitely	Mostly	Sometimes	Not at all
24	I have people who understand and support me	Definitely	Mostly	Sometimes	Not at all
25	I can make positive goals for the future	Definitely	Mostly	Sometimes	Not at all

Client's signature: .... Therapist's signature: ....

From 'not at all' to 'definitely' – exploring the four point scale

Each choice the client makes between 'not at all' and 'definitely' represents their unique perspective. Their choice is not in any sense objective and the reasons for it are entirely relative to the meanings they ascribe to the activities and their level of function. This should not be seen as a disadvantage, however. It is the possibility of engaging with people's unique meanings that ensures a client-centred focus and a conversation about occupation rather than simply activity and skills. This subjectivity is the same as when using scaling in a solution focused conversation as detailed in Chapter One. For example, a client who exercises once a week may choose 'definitely' for 'I take regular exercise' whereas another client may think exercising once a week only warrants 'sometimes'. Each choice out of the four options gives rise to general possibilities of holding a solution focused conversation.

It is also important to find out whether a client is content with being at a particular point on the scale. Not everyone wants to change and therapists should guard against assuming that all clients want to be able to respond 'definitely' to every statement on the Measure.

In order to develop solution focused conversation around the client's choices and relate to them as relative points on a scale, here are some useful strategies.

'Not at all'

If the client has clarified that they are not satisfied with being at this point on the scale, the therapist can begin by acknowledging how difficult that part of their life might be. Depending on the category the therapist might say something like:

– That sounds rather difficult for you, how do you cope? Who or what helps you to cope?

Since some clients may respond 'not at all' because they are feeling hopeless or finding it hard to see anything positive in their lives, the therapist can gently probe for exceptions:

– Are there any times at all when you are able to do… even in a

really small way, even if it's only occasionally?
- When was the last time you were able to do...? What was happening at that time that enabled that to happen? What was different about that time?
- If I asked someone who knows you well, where would they place you on the scale?
- If I had asked you this question at another time in your life when things were different, what would you have said?
- What would you be doing differently if you'd felt able to respond 'sometimes'?
- What might be the first small sign that you are moving from 'not at all' towards 'sometimes'?

Sometimes

Choosing this option means that the therapist can begin to identify exceptions, or times when the desired behaviour is beginning to happen and build on these exceptions. The therapist can ask:
- How do you do that?
- What is happening that's different when you do ... sometimes?
- Who or what helps you to do ... sometimes?
- What are you doing differently when you are able to ...?
- What would people who know you say you were doing differently when you are able to ...?
- What do you notice about the times when you are able to ...?
- I'm impressed that you're able to do ... even if it's only sometimes, how do you do that?
- What would it take for you to be able to move from 'sometimes' to 'mostly'?
- What would be the first small sign that you are moving from 'sometimes' towards 'mostly'?

Mostly and Definitely

When a client chooses 'mostly' or 'definitely' as an option to one of the statements, this is an area where the therapist can build on the client's strengths and successes. The therapist can ask:

- I'm impressed that you are able to do … most of the time, how do you do that?
- Are you satisfied with your ability to do … or would you like to improve?
- How could your ability to do … help you to improve other areas?
- Have you always been able to do … or is it something you've learned or developed?
- If so, how, or from whom?
- Could that help you now?
- What advice would that person give you now to help you achieve the changes you want to make?

Exploring the detail of everyday life – the 25 statements

There are 25 statements that the client should rate in relation to their perception of themselves. While the principles of working with the four-point scale described above can be applied to all the questions, the following descriptions expand the purpose and possibilities of the statements. To encourage each component to be fully explored there are some suggested supplementary questions that can be asked to aid the solution focused process. At the very least it is assumed that people will not have the same level of problems in every area, so there are bound to be opportunities for discussion of strengths and success.

The relevant area of function is noted in brackets after the question.

1. I am able to talk to people *(Communication)*

This was chosen as the first question because if the client has agreed to participate in the interview then they are already showing an ability to talk to people. Therefore the answer to this question is not likely to be 'not at all', allowing the conversation to start with a positive note. If someone does answer 'not at all', the fact that they are talking to the therapist is a ready-made exception which the therapist can use. For example:

> – Well, you are managing to talk to me, so I'm wondering why
> you've chosen 'not at all'.

This curiosity opens the possibility of a conversation about what the client thinks 'talking to people' means. Sometimes people's own definitions lead them to discount times when they are, in fact, talking to people. Asking what would be happening at 'definitely' can clarify the client's meanings.

> – So what would you be doing differently if you'd chosen
> 'definitely'?

The client's answers may lead to many different aspects of communication. For example, clients may refer to specific situations such as talking to people in authority, or they may focus on how they would feel, for instance confident or assertive. Other responses may relate to getting across one's ideas or getting people to understand them. With this information, the therapist can now begin to look for some exceptions.

> – Can you tell me about times, maybe from the past, when you
> have been able to get your ideas across?

or they could ask:

> – So what would you notice that would tell you that you were
> able to 'get your ideas across most of the time'?

The single quotation marks above denote the therapist using the client's language which is strongly recommended and preferable to paraphrasing.

If the client identifies this area as a priority to work on, they may go on to consider the small steps that would let them know they were moving towards the next stage on the Measure. These may then be translated into goals.

Information that may arise as a result of asking these questions and might lead the occupational therapist to offer some practical help or advice once the specific area of need is identified by the client. For example, help with assertiveness or confidence-building, or even a referral to a speech therapist.

2. I have satisfying relationships *(Relationships)*

Relationships are a central part of all human life. This question can include relationships with family members, partner, friends, work and social contacts. It may highlight the ability to form and maintain relationships. Relating to others is possibly the most important part of someone's life and is often the major source of thinking about 'who we are', therefore the importance of exploring relationships should not be minimised.

In solution focused brief therapy the power of relationships is often highlighted through third-party questioning. For example, after any discussion of a desired change the therapist can ask a question along the lines of:

– When you are doing (desired change) what will your (spouse/parent/sibling/other important relationship) notice?
– How might they respond differently? or
– What might they do differently?

For many people relationships are a source of support and affirmation, but they can also be a source of conflict and stress. Relationships are a complex and important aspect of life for everyone but mental health service users have various additional difficulties in their relationships.

Stigma and misunderstanding in society regarding mental distress can affect the way people react and respond to people with mental distress within all sorts of relationships from immediate family to the workplace. Because of this, some of the ways that people behave or show their feelings when they are under strain or in distress can lead to problems within relationships, such as aggression, humiliation, rejection, social isolation or being ignored or discounted. It is important to bear this in mind when asking this question so that the therapist does not give the impression that difficulties with relationships are the sole responsibility of the client. One way of doing this is to ask, for example:

– When you are at 'mostly' what will other people be doing differently?

If the answer suggests that the client is currently not been treated respectfully by someone the therapist could explore this further:

– Does that mean your brother shouts a lot at you at the

moment? That sounds unpleasant, how do you cope with it?
The conversation could then follow on to finding exceptions:

– Can you tell me about any times when you manage to have a
  pleasant time with your brother? What is different about those
  times?

The answers to this question may give clues to how the client might
handle the situation differently, either by modifying their own behaviour
or perhaps realising that it is best to avoid the other person at certain
times.

This question could also lead to discussions regarding roles. For
example, there are often tensions within families where parents, siblings
or a spouse has taken on the role of carer. This can make it hard for the
client to regain their roles as they begin to take back control of their
lives.

3. I have confidence in myself *(Confidence)*

Many people who have experienced acute mental distress suffer a loss of
confidence. Rebuilding confidence is a hugely important factor when
dealing with or recovering from a period of using mental health services.
A large majority of people cite a need to gain confidence as a major
factor in their recovery.

An episode of mental distress can lead someone to question a lot
of basic assumptions they hold about themselves. There are things we
take for granted in life, such as our ability to cope and to remain self-
sufficient. Many people do not imagine that they will ever need support
from professional services.

A period of reduced mental health affects a number of areas of our
lives. It is likely that a person will have withdrawn from their normal
routine and daily functioning. Additionally they may have stopped
undertaking their usual roles and responsibilities. Loss of routine, even
for a short time, can affect one's perception of self and may lead to self-
doubt. It is very common for someone to be unsure about how they
will cope during recovery from an episode of acute distress. Questions
that may be useful are:

– How will you know when you are coping better?

- What will you be doing differently?
- What will other people notice about you?

If a person has been in hospital (whether formally or informally) it can have a particularly damaging effect on confidence. In this situation people can experience a lack of control and may have had decisions made on their behalf. Hospitalisation in a mental health facility is still a stigma in our society. People may feel that others are questioning their ability, which will cause increased self-doubt. In addition we all have our own perception of what it means to have suffered a period of mental distress, and this will need to be addressed.

Confidence means different things to different people and this needs to be explored in detail with each individual. Questions that may be useful to aid exploration of this are:

- When you are feeling more confident, what will you be doing?
- What will others notice about you when you have more confidence?
- How will you know when your confidence is returning?

4. I can stand up for myself *(Assertiveness)*

Being able to stand one's ground without giving in or losing one's temper is a life skill that is increasingly recognised as contributing to effective communication and the development of self-confidence. As a concept it has become more widely recognised by the general public through assertiveness training courses, which have been reported in the media as a subject of both interest and derision.

While psychologists view assertiveness as the 'adult' way of getting what you want or standing up for yourself, many people feel uncomfortable with the idea of assertiveness and equate it with being 'pushy'. When discussing this question with a client it is therefore important to ensure that you are working with the client's idea of standing up for themselves, at least as a starting point.

Some further questions that could be useful when discussing this might be:

- Are there any situations where you would like to stand up for yourself more?

- What will you be doing differently?

People often do not want to stand up for themselves because it might affect their image of themselves. You might ask:

- When you are standing up for yourself, how will you be feeling?

If the client then responds with a negative feeling, you could ask:

- How could you stand up for yourself and feel OK about doing it?

Another reason that people do not stand up for themselves is fear of the reactions of others. You might ask:

- When you are standing up for yourself, what will other people notice?

or

- When you are standing up for yourself, how might other people respond?

It is important to move at the client's own pace in this area. If the client identifies it as an area of desired change, provision of or referral to assertiveness training could be beneficial.

5. I am able to make decisions when I need to *(Decision Making)*

This question follows on from the previous question. Making a decision is about having confidence in making or expressing choices. People who suffer from episodes of mental distress often have decisions made for them and might be given the message that they cannot trust themselves. While this may be true at certain times within a period of difficulty coping with mental distress, the majority of the time people are capable of knowing what they want. Taking away their choice may lead to lack of confidence in making decisions.

Occupational therapists are interested in decision-making because of its close relationship to occupational performance. When people lose the ability to make decisions their function becomes limited. Occupations requiring greater decision-making ability may be the first to be affected, such as at work. It is not unusual to encounter people who have gradually lost roles as they increasingly avoid taking responsibility for making decisions.

If people answer 'not at all' to this question it may be that they lack confidence in making major life decisions. It can be helpful to focus on exceptions by asking about small everyday decisions. Even in a hospital environment such as an acute inpatient unit a person may exert their choice in a variety of small ways on a daily basis. Focusing on a person's ability to make smaller decisions could restore confidence or provide a foundation for making larger ones. When a small decision has been identified, you can ask:

– How did you do that?

This question is very useful in eliciting a person's particular way of making decisions.

Another way of starting this type of conversation is to ask:

– How have you made big decisions in the past?

or

– What or who has helped you make big decisions in the past?

Drawing on people's past success could be achieved by asking:

– What decisions have you made in the past that you are proud of?

All of these questions can be followed up by asking for details of the individual way that decisions are made. For example, people might discuss how their beliefs and values play a part, or that there are certain people they trust for advice. There are many other sources that people use such as books or even reading Tarot cards.

6. I am satisfied with my home environment *(Environment)*

Gaining a picture of how a person's environment is unique to them will contribute towards an understanding of their situation as a whole. As occupational therapists we consider the relationship between the person and their environment to be an inseparable interplay. People respond to and are influenced by their environment and this shapes the patterns of everyday activities as well as affecting motivation to carry them out. The environment also plays a large part in maintaining the habitual performance of occupations by providing familiar cues.

If a person is not comfortable or able to function in their environment it will significantly affect their ability to engage in activities of daily living. An example of this is a person who was suffering from feelings of paranoia and could not leave the house for fear of contact with the neighbours. This meant reduced independence as she was unable to carry out basic everyday tasks such as hanging out the washing or putting out the bins. She was reliant on her daughter's help which affected her feelings of self-worth.

Environmental issues may affect a person's mood for a number of reasons. For example, noisy or hostile neighbours or overcrowded conditions can be a considerable cause of stress. In addition, a person's physical health may suffer if there are environmental health issues such as damp or unhygienic surroundings.

It is not uncommon when a person is extremely distressed for them to retreat into their living space and damage or deface their surroundings. This in turn will have an effect on maintaining occupational performance.

If a person answers 'not at all' to this question you could ask the following:
- When things feel at their worst, what do you do that enables you to cope?
- Are there times when the difficult things about your environment affect you less?
- What resources are available to you to resolve this difficult situation?

Other questions that may be used for other responses are:
- Imagine you are satisfied with your home environment… Tell me what that environment would look like.
- What small changes could you begin to make to feel more comfortable at home?

7. I am able to take care of the place where I live, including laundry, shopping and cooking (Domestic Activities of Daily Living) and

8. I can take care of myself, e.g. personal hygiene tasks (Personal Activities of Daily Living)
These two questions are considered together.

Activities of Daily Living are a major domain of concern for occupational therapists as they form the detail everyday life. Occupational therapists understand that each person has unique personal preferences in carrying out daily living tasks and that there may be factors which promote or limit their success in doing so. For example, a student living in a shared house may find it harder than a person living alone in a flat to carry out domestic daily living tasks in the way they would like. However, the student may have more skills than the person living alone. A highly competent office worker may find it hard to get washed and dressed if they have become depressed despite having been able to do this automatically when well.

Being able to carry out daily living tasks is recognised by occupational therapists as a central part of self-care. In turn, self-care is the foundation for other aspects of occupation such as leisure and work activities. Caring for oneself and one's immediate environment are such basic life skills that major problems in this area can be considered an indication of risk behaviour, such as self-neglect or potential damage to health.

It is not unusual for people who are suffering from mental distress to have difficulties in both personal and domestic activities of daily living. This could be through a lack of motivation caused by mental disturbances such as depression or because a person is preoccupied with hallucinations. Sometimes people who have had multiple and lengthy admissions to hospital since early adulthood have never learned or consolidated necessary skills. Somebody who is emerging from an episode of mental distress may have lost confidence in carrying out occupations that were previously habitual.

Responses to the miracle question and other future-oriented questions often refer to daily living tasks, such as tidying the home, getting food and other basic routines. Through asking someone to describe their miracle day in detail they are carrying out an occupational analysis for themselves. This means that the occupational therapist may not have to undertake a lengthy assessment process, essentially allowing the client to provide a picture of their preferred level of self-care and domestic activities and skills. It is not unusual for a solution focused brief therapist who is not an occupational therapist to ask for a high level of detail of a daily living task, such as how the client makes breakfast. This course of questioning resonates well with occupational therapy. The major difference is that through asking the client to describe daily living tasks in this way, the client also can identify the goals and methods for achieving them. This means that the time and energy of the occupational therapist can be focused on helping with specific areas of improvement that will really make a difference.

Case 9 Bridget

Bridget is a young woman with a history of schizophrenia and identified as having mild learning difficulties. She lives in a one-bedroom flat in a warden-controlled complex. She has lived there for two years and has managed independently during this time. The occupational therapist received a referral from the social worker who was concerned that Bridget was becoming increasingly anxious and complaining that she could no longer manage her flat.

When the occupational therapist visited, the flat appeared clean and tidy but Bridget was very agitated and eager to communicate how bad things were so the therapist decided to ask:

THERAPIST: On a scale of 0–10, where 0 is you feel completely unable to cope with taking care of your home and 10 is you feel totally confident about it, where are you now?

BRIDGET: About 7.

THERAPIST: 7? Wow that's pretty good. How do you know you're at 7?

(Bridget gave a long list of all the household tasks she was happy undertaking)

THERAPIST: OK, so can you tell me about what would be different when you're at 10?

BRIDGET: I'd be able to keep my bathroom clean and do my laundry.

At this point the occupational therapist asked Bridget to show her the bathroom and where she did the washing. The bathroom was not dirty, apart from the wash hand-basin area, which was covered in cosmetic bottles. Bridget complained that she could not clean the basin. She was able to use her washing-machine without a problem but she showed the occupational therapist a huge pile of washed clothes on her spare bed which she felt overwhelmed by. Because of her learning difficulties, Bridget had not been able to problem-solve these situations and it is in these circumstances that the expertise of the occupational therapist can be used to collaborate in meeting the client's goals. Through discussion and negotiation the occupational therapist brought a small plastic basket in which Bridget could store her toiletries instead of storing them around the hand-basin. She was then able to keep the basin clean. The occupational therapist spent an afternoon with Bridget sorting out her washing and putting it away into drawers and wardrobes. She then brought a large plastic washing-basket and devised a routine using the basket so Bridget could keep her laundry under control.

A few weeks later the social worker reported that Bridget's anxiety had disappeared and she had returned to her former happy self. It is interesting to speculate that if she had been visited by someone with a problem-focused style, Bridget's anxiety might have been the focus of attention and intervention may have resulted in her being offered anxiety management, medication or even admission to hospital. In this example, Bridget was able to identify 'the difference that would make a difference'. Through using a solution focused approach the occupational therapist was able to quickly find the occupational performance area that was causing difficulties and use their expertise to solve the problem.

If people respond with 'not at all' and 'sometimes', the therapist can also draw on exceptions in the questions they are asking:

- What are you managing to do, however small, at the moment?
- Can you tell me a bit about what areas, however small, you are managing well at the moment?
- What were you doing when you felt you were managing these areas well?
- What will you be doing when you are definitely able to manage these areas?

The last two questions above draw out the person's subjective view of how they prefer to carry out activities of daily living. Occupational therapists are aware that people have different standards and preferences in activities of daily living, but it is worth emphasising the importance of not imposing one's own standards on our clients. Unless there is a concern that a person is at risk though self-neglect, clients have the right to manage themselves and their homes as they wish. You could ask a client if they are satisfied with the way they carry out these activities.

Since both domestic and personal activities of daily living may affect relationships, if a client is discussing a desire for change, a third-party question can be useful:

- When you are definitely taking care of yourself and your home as you want to, how might (other people) respond?

As with all future or outcome orientated questions, it can be followed up with:

- What difference will that make?

Success in carrying out daily living tasks depends on many of the factors that are explored elsewhere in the Measure, such as organisation, routine, decision-making and problem-solving. This can be utilised in building exceptions when asking these questions.

9. I can manage my finances (Budgeting)

People who use mental health services often have difficulties in the area of financial management. These can arise for a variety of reasons.

Some difficulties are related to employment. Episodes of mental distress may have affected a person's ability to work, hold on to a job or progress to a better-paid job. Consequently many people have to live on a very low wage. Because so many people with long-term mental health difficulties are unemployed they have to rely on state benefits.

Budgeting on a low income is very difficult and failure to do this is often the reason that people who use mental health services struggle to live independently as bills mount up and services are cut off. This is a risk for anyone on a low income, but for the mental health service user it is often accompanied by problems such as difficulty organising thoughts, preoccupation with other issues, low mood and energy, episodes of reckless spending or lack of acquired skills.

If the answer to this question is 'not at all', it is important to explore whether the respondent has previous ability. If not, and this is identified as an area for desired change, the occupational therapist may choose an educational approach, such as teaching money management skills. If there is previous ability, this can be explored to provide evidence of skill and consequently built on. Some helpful questions may be:

- When you are able to manage your money well, what will you be doing?
- What difference will that make?

Worksheet Q9 has been used with this question. It asks 'What do you have to spend money on?' in order to provide information for budgeting. However, it also asks, 'What do you like to spend money on?' The responses to this question are more qualitative and give clues to what a person values and desires, which in turn link to personal meanings.

- What is/will be different when you are able to spend your money on…?

Using solution focused questions in this area can help to increase motivation and looks beyond simple skill acquisition to the wider meanings associated with money.

10. I can organise my week in a way that works for me/satisfies me *(Organisation/Routine)*

Routine is often disturbed through a period of mental distress. This may be due to a variety of factors ranging from the effects of mental distress to loss of roles which have previously provided structure.

The importance of routine is discussed widely in occupational therapy theory. Performing occupations on a habitual basis strengthens ability, confidence and motivation to continue doing them. When people establish a routine that suits them, carrying out daily occupations becomes more fluent. They do not have to think about them so much and in turn, activities and decisions which are out of the ordinary are easier to undertake.

While the question asks about organising a whole week, it is useful to search for exceptions by looking for any evidence of routine.

- What activities, however small, do you carry out on a regular basis?

Since people prefer different levels or types of routine, you could ask:

- Can you describe what a satisfying weekly routine would look like for you?

The types of answer may reflect preferences such as order, balance or opportunities for spontaneity.

11. I can get to where I want/need to go *(Mobility)*

If a person is unable to get to where they want or need to go it may be the result of a number of issues. These may include physical limitations, anxiety, a lack of resources, such as transport, money or someone to accompany them or living in an environment that feels unsafe due to crime, anti-social behaviour or poor lighting.

Before trying to construct solutions for difficulties in this area it could be helpful to find out where people need to go and how life would be different when they are able to do so. This can raise motivation to set goals and define small steps. Some questions that could be asked are:

- What will be different when you are able to get where you want (need) to go?
- Can you tell me about a time when getting to… was easier for you?
- What was different (what were you doing) when you were able to do this?
- What skills or resources were you using then that you could use again now?

12. I am able to calm myself when needed *(Anxiety Management)*

The feelings we label as 'anxiety', which include dread and foreboding, racing negative thoughts, heightened awareness, unpleasant physical sensations such as pounding heart, breathing too fast and even chest pain, are part of our normal response to threat or perceived threat. As an evolutionary adaptation, this response helps us to escape from attack or to fight off predators. In the modern world, where we are unlikely to meet a lion around the corner, this response is still triggered when we perceive a threat. This could take various different forms for example, the threat of loss if we find out a loved one is ill, the threat to our livelihood in a workplace where redundancy is rumoured, the threat to our security if every month we barely manage to pay the rent. All these can evoke feelings of anxiety which are identical to those elicited by the lion around the corner.

Acute feelings of anxiety are very unpleasant and some people think they are experiencing a serious medical crisis such as a heart attack. When this happens people perceive the anxiety response itself as a threat and their solution is to avoid any situation where that response will be triggered. This is often the root of phobias.

It is also normal to feel anxious in a new or unfamiliar situation. People who have been disengaged from everyday life may feel anxious when trying to regain roles and re-engage in activities or learning new ones in order to make changes.

Many people who seek help from mental health services have difficulties with anxiety which interfere with everyday life, so this question offers the opportunity to have conversations which can normalise the experience or generate alternative solutions. Some people will answer 'not at all' because they feel they are anxious all the time or because they think they cannot cope with acute anxiety. It can be helpful to try to elicit a time when the problem is less acute:

- You say you are anxious all the time, so could you tell me about a time in the day when your anxiety is less troublesome to you?

This question acknowledges their experience but may also provide a first step to breaking down an all-pervasive sense of constant anxiety.

In order to explore a possible future without anxiety, one could ask:

- What will you be doing when you are able to calm yourself?

This allows a focus on the occupations which are important to the person and can help to develop courage and motivation to change. Small steps can also be generated if the client wishes to change.

Using the four stages of the Measure as a scale can be particularly effective by eliciting what would be different at 'sometimes', 'mostly' and 'definitely'. As anxiety often affects personal and social relationships, third-person questions can help, such as:

 – When you are at 'mostly' what difference will (other people) notice about you

13. I have positive ways of coping with angry feelings
(Anger Management)

Anger and anger management are areas of importance to general mental health practice primarily because of the association with violence. While the public often unfairly associate angry and violent behaviour with 'mental illness', there are a significant minority of service users for whom such behaviour is an issue. Their expression of anger and violence may result from hearing voices, being frustrated, or misinterpreting others' behaviour. Much of the risk assessment carried out in practice is to minimise any potential for violence.

However, angry feelings can in themselves be very distressing. Aside from the emotional distress, there are also associated physiological symptoms which cause stress, and as a result anger is often accompanied by feelings of anxiety. For different reasons anger also affects people's ability to undertake occupations, and can be a paralysing emotion that reduces motivation and interferes with social and work relationships. In adolescents it can interfere with education, leading to exclusion. It can also be directed inward through self-harming activities such as substance misuse, cutting and suicide attempts. This contributes to the importance of considering anger when assessing risk.

Having said that, anger is a normal human emotion, and many people who use mental health services have a lot to be angry about. They might be experiencing prejudice and discrimination in everyday life due to the stigma associated with mental health difficulties, or they might be misunderstood by family and friends. Their views are often not sought by professionals trying to help them, and some of the treatment they receive at in-patient units is less than respectful, restrictive or frightening. Admittance under a Section of the Mental Health Act is experienced as a gross loss of liberty and is sometimes carried out with physical force.

When discussing this question it is important to clarify that a 'positive way' of coping is any way that does not involve self-harm or harming others. This provides a normalising view of anger and can elicit many creative and useful solutions.

If a respondent replies 'not at all' to this question, it is a strong indication that there may be a risk and should be taken seriously. The therapist should spend some time to find some exceptions, however small.

There are usually times when it is easier to control one's anger, and it is helpful to explore this. For example, certain friends or environments, times of the day or levels of energy are calming and can provide exceptions that break down a feeling of lack of control over anger.

It is usual for people to see the solution to angry feelings as 'stopping feeling angry or being angry'. This is similar to other unwanted behaviour or emotions. When working in a solution focused way, we are looking for concrete observable changes rather than the absence of something. Something you 'won't be doing' needs to be replaced by what you 'will be doing'. The therapist can ask:

- When you are coping positively with anger, what will you be doing differently
- When you are not responding with feelings of anger, what will be you doing instead?

Looking for what people will be doing 'instead' is very useful if, in response to being asked what they will be doing at 'mostly' or 'always', they say 'I won't be shouting', 'I won't be reaching for a drink', 'I won't be cutting myself' and so on.

"What will you be doing instead of shouting" and similar questions invite people to construct positive responses and behaviour for themselves. They are more likely to try out new behaviour if they have thought of it themselves. Likewise, their solutions will probably be workable because they know their own situations better than the therapist can hope to.

If people have difficulty identifying positive alternatives you can look for examples from elsewhere:

- Can you tell me about ways of dealing with anger that other people you know use?

– Who inspires you most with their ability to deal with anger?

For adolescents and children, using references to characters from books or television can bring many useful examples.

If people respond to this question with 'sometimes', the therapist should be very interested in how they do this and try to elicit a lot of detail. This will reinforce the respondent's sense of control. Although not strictly solution-focused, using a question that externalises the angry feelings will also help weaken the identification with the emotion.

– When anger takes hold, what do you do/can you do to regain control?

The benefits of managing anger can be explored through using third-party questions:

– What will your family notice about you when you start managing your anger more effectively?

– How will people close to you treat you differently when you are doing this

14. I am able to achieve what I set out to do *(Positive Focus)*

This area is a central concern for occupational therapists. It is best described in the Model of Human Occupation *(Kielhofner, 2002)* as an interplay between volition, habituation and performance capacity. Volition is what impels us to do things and is closely linked to values, beliefs and motivation. Habituation is related to the patterns we establish to make everyday occupation possible. Performance capacity is a combination of internal factors such as mental and physical ability as well as the external structures that support or limit occupation.

People who use mental health services may be experiencing difficulties in many of these areas and the occupational therapist can explore these while discussing this question. For example in a person with depression, volition may be affected by low mood which results in negative thinking such as 'it's not worth it, I can't do anything right.' Habituation may be affected by low energy and resultant inability to carry out daily living tasks. Habit is a powerful motivator and once broken, it can be hard to re-establish. Performance capacity may be affected by low energy so the person tires easily. They may have lost touch with people with whom they carry out activities, hence something as simple as losing a regular lift to the shops can prevent them from engaging in a previously valued occupation.

When discussing this, the occupational therapist will be able to look for exceptions in a wide variety of areas due to this complex understanding of occupation. They can explore what motivates occupational choices, how people plan, how they put a plan into action, how they consider resources, time span and whether the goals set are realistic.

If a respondent answers 'not at all' to this question, the occupational therapist can draw exceptions from simply looking at any everyday activity, for example:

- What did you have to do to get ready to come to this appointment? How did you do that?

This question is a good one in which to explore small steps because of the focus on achievement.

- What small goal can you set that would let you feel you were moving towards 'sometimes' (or 'mostly' and 'definitely')?

If the difficulty is in the area of volition, the therapist could ask:

- What helps/would help you decide what to do?
- When you can achieve what you set out to do, what will your life be like?

If it is habituation:

- How often would you have to do this to feel confident you will continue doing this?

If it is performance capacity:

- What practical help might you need to carry this out?

This question is also closely linked to problem-solving and decision-making which are addressed by questions 4 and 15.

15. I am able to maintain my concentration and attention on activities that are important to me (Concentration)

It is very common for people with mental distress to experience difficulties with concentration. There are a number of factors that affect concentration, such as anxiety, lack of sleep, certain prescribed medication and general feelings of lethargy.

It is important to ascertain what concentration means to an individual. This can be difficult to quantify. It may be useful to help examine times of the day when a person finds it easier to concentrate, and to explore what is different at those times. An example of a question you could ask is:

— Has there been a time in your life when you found it easier to concentrate?
— What was different at this time?

If somebody answers never, and this is an area of concern for them, it will be helpful to give the corresponding worksheet for a homework task.

16. I am able to solve problems as they arise *(Problem-Solving)*

This area is linked with confidence and self-belief. Generally when people are well they are able to solve problems as they arise, either independently or with the help of others around them. They may also be able to seek help appropriately and access resources to aid them in their problem-solving.

When someone is experiencing mental distress the process of solving a problem can become harder. A situation that was previously easy to solve may be catastrophised, which could lead to feelings of panic and a reduced ability of the normal cognitive process to find solutions. It may result in a lack of concentration, ability to sequence or the confidence ask for help. Sometimes a person may be able to solve some problems but find that more complex ones are harder to solve. Consequently feelings of panic may occur earlier than previously.

If the response to this question is 'sometimes', 'mostly' or 'definitely' you could ask:

— How did you do that?
— What skills were you using?

If the response is 'never' you could look for exceptions and draw on past competence:

— What is the biggest problem you've ever solved?
— What did it take for you to do that?
— What did you learn about yourself that could be useful now?

17. I can get so involved in a project or activity that I can forget about my discomfort *(Activity Engagement)*

The idea that engaging in activity has a beneficial or therapeutic effect is central to occupational therapy *(Reilly, 1962)*. In this question, the therapist can explore how some activities have the potential to draw in the participant to the extent that they are distracted from their concerns or discomfort. They might say they were 'lost in a book' or completely absorbed by a television programme or jigsaw puzzle. These times give the potential for discussing exceptions to when a person's problems are perceived to be happening, and can contribute to a conversation whereby the client begins to experience their problems as less constant or unchanging.

The benefits of engaging in an occupation are linked to the level of interest or significance of the occupation for the participant *(Rebeiro and Cook, 1999)*. One can take this further and see the process in terms of stages whereby a person participating in an activity that interests them becomes engaged by it, leading to absorption *(Burgess, 2004)*. This is when the process becomes therapeutic and has occupational significance. What is interesting is that virtually any activity has this potential. For some people ordinary household tasks such as washing-up or ironing are often described as 'therapeutic'. For others it will be something more recognised as leisure, such as the cinema or gardening. For occupational therapists, linking into the significance an occupation has, or potentially may have, for their clients and then grading the activity to prevent boredom or excess challenge, is key to a successful collaboration. Discussions around this question can explore which activities are significant to the respondent.

People with mental distress can lose touch with activities that are absorbing. This may be because they have become over-focused on their own thoughts or because they have gradually stopped doing things. When people are in an in-patient unit they do not have access to their everyday activities within a familiar context. With a lessening of participation and engagement in activities, motivation to begin an activity is reduced creating a cycle of apathy and inactivity. In order to restart a positive engagement, finding stimulating and interesting things for people to do is dependent on exploring activities that have potential for absorption.

When phrasing this question the authors have found it useful to replace the word 'discomfort' with a more specific term, such as anxiety or depression, when a clear difficulty has already been identified by the individual. Questions that may be helpful to ask are:

- What activities do you do that take your mind off your problems?
- Have you ever found yourself so absorbed in doing something that you lost track of time?
- What is it about these activities that interests you/is important to you?

18. I am able to contribute to meeting the needs of my family *(Family Needs)*

When people experience mental distress it can lead to withdrawal from family life, reduced contact or an inability to maintain roles and responsibilities within the family. Guilt is often expressed by people in this situation since they may feel they are letting their family down. Because families are dynamic systems, other members will adapt to cope and this may make it hard for someone to regain their roles and responsibilities when they feel more able.

'Needs' is a general term and means many different things to different people. The occupational therapist will need to spend time exploring what 'contributing to meeting needs' means to the individual. People may have quite limited views of what it means, so discussion could also open up possibilities of seeing needs in a different way. For example, if the respondent saw their role as providing an income, the therapist could ask about emotional or recreational needs. Doing this could provide some exceptions to build on. This can also be a useful time to build an understanding of their unique family lives and their commitments and support networks. Questions that may be useful are:

- What do you do for your family at present, however small?
- What does your family need you to do? What part of this are you doing already?

- What will you be doing differently when you are able to meet the needs of your family?
- What will your family see you doing when you are meetings their needs more effectively?
- What difference will this make?

19. I am able to function adequately at work (*Work Skills*)
and
20. I would like to be able to work or retrain (*Work/Training*)
Work is generally recognised as an important occupation for most people. Work brings many benefits, such as a sense of productivity, routine, recognition, self-development, status and, of course, income. Since being employed is seen as desirable to an individual and society, unemployment is strongly linked to social exclusion. Finding or returning to work can be a difficult process for people who have experienced or have ongoing mental distress and combating this has become a government priority *(Social Exclusion Unit, 2003)*. Occupational therapists are seen as key contributors to helping people with mental health issues gain employment *(The College of Occupational Therapists and The Royal College of Psychiatrists, 2002)*.

Someone who is unemployed and has recently suffered from mental distress may feel under pressure to return to work or to retrain. They may see themselves as unsuccessful if they are not employed. It can be useful to check with individuals that they are not simply responding to this question in the 'right' way.

If either of these areas is highlighted by the individual as something they choose to work on further, it may be helpful to explore positive experiences of work they have had in the past. It will be useful to have a discussion around a person's work history and their skills and achievements. Questions that can be asked are:

- When you were functioning well at work, what were you doing?
- Can you give me an example of when you do these things now, even in a small way?

The worksheet that accompanies this question can be particularly useful in exploring an individual's motivational factors.

There are many new initiatives, both voluntary and government-funded, to help people return to education and work. These can be useful contacts if this is one of their goals.

21. I can enjoy myself *(Enjoyment)*

Enjoyment and pleasure have a positive impact on all areas of a person's life. However, engaging in activities in the areas of work and self-care may also produce enjoyment and pleasure.

When in mental distress people lose touch with their positive experiences and their ability to reach a state of enjoyment, they may feel that it is unimportant to try. They may find that basic functioning on a day-to-day basis is enough to cope with and the idea of seeking pleasure may be unimaginable. It is important therefore to seek out exceptions.

– What small things do you find pleasure in doing?
– What would be the most enjoyable day you could imagine?
– What sorts of things have you enjoyed in the past?

It may be useful to follow these questions with further exploration of the skills required to achieve a sense of enjoyment.

– What were you doing to create a sense of enjoyment?

This should help the person see that they have some control over making pleasurable experiences happen. It also produces a feeling of empowerment.

22. I take regular exercise *(Exercise)*

It is not uncommon for someone experiencing mental distress to have lost, or never developed, a regular exercise routine. Often people may have an altered perception of their body image. They may lack confidence in their body and in their ability to perform physical tasks. There may have been a change in their normal routine of physical activity or exercise due to lack of motivation, low mood and energy levels, or even practical issues, such as lack of company, transport or local amenities. Some psychotropic medications lead to weight gain which in turn reduces confidence and motivation.

However, while overcoming mental distress can seem like a big hurdle, taking control of one's physical well-being may be a more achievable goal and can often be a first step to gaining control over other areas of life.

Engagement in physical activity has a huge range of benefits, including the positive feeling that results when you have exercised, the social interaction that may be a part of the activity and, if participating in a team sport, the feeling of belonging, making a difference and of being needed. Exercising may also give someone something to talk about and look forward to. Exercise can be as simple as a regular walk to the local shop or can become a project whereby one is aiming to improve performance through practice. Supporting questions that could be asked are:

 – What is different when you feel motivated to exercise?
 – What benefits do you notice when you take regular exercise?
If appropriate,
 – When you exercised regularly, how did you stay motivated to continue?

23. I get enough rest and sleep *(Rest/Sleep)*

People who use mental health services often complain of problems related to sleeping. Sometimes it is regarding difficulty getting to sleep, often associated with racing thoughts, or complaining of waking early in the morning, which is usually associated with depressed mood. Some people lose a normal pattern of waking and sleeping, for example getting up later and later and then going to bed later. This can affect their ability to participate in everyday life as they miss things happening during the day, such as work, family contact, shopping and so on, and this then becomes harder to re-establish as routines are lost. Lack of sleep will have physiological and psychological effects such as tiredness, lack of concentration and irritability. Some people spend too much time asleep or resting, often as a side effect of medication but also through gradual withdrawal from occupations and habit formation. Of course, some people have lost work, social contacts and daily routines through admission to hospital and this has contributed to increased time spent in bed or resting. The resultant lack of fitness and low energy levels often affect motivation and confidence to re-engage with valued occupations such as work and domestic activities of daily living. Some simple questions that can be asked are:

- What is different when you manage to get enough rest and sleep?
- What have you done when you get a good night's sleep?
- What strategies did you use in the past to fall asleep?
- What small step could you take to help get back to sleeping and waking at times that suit you better?

24. I have people who understand and support me *(Support Networks)*

It is common when people are experiencing mental distress for them to feel isolated and misunderstood. It can be hard explain feelings and experiences to people who have not had similar difficulties. Friends and family who may have been supportive in the past can find it difficult to listen to feelings of distress. When faced with these issues it can be hard for people to talk openly and trust others.

Some people may not be able to easily identify the support that is available to them and may benefit from discussions around this. Others may want to explore new support networks. Questions that may be useful to ask:

- What difference would it make if you had people who understood and supported you?
- Are there any people who give you support, even in a small way?

If somebody replied 'not at all' to this question it may be helpful to ask:

- What does support mean to you?
- If you had support, what would it look like?

25. I can make positive goals for the future *(Hopefulness)*

This statement was deliberately placed at the end of the measure as it was seen as a good way of creating an ending that could lead to goal-setting discussions. It can also create a useful lead in terms of summarising the

Measure and previous discussions.

It is important to have a sense of our future and a belief that we can influence our destiny. As individuals we need to experience our actions as having some positive effect on the future. It is common for people who have been suffering mental distress to experience low self-esteem and struggle with maintaining a positive future focus.

If somebody were to answer 'Never' to this statement, it could be useful to review and expand on questions 1–24 where an individual may have touched on areas where a future focus was evident.

If a response falls in the categories 'Definitely', 'Mostly' or 'Sometimes' then goals can be explored. (It may be useful at this point for the therapist to review Chapter One, which offers ideas about how to enable people to set goals). A question that may be used could be:

– What sort of plans are you making at the moment?

Responses to this statement may also highlight whether the therapist needs to be concerned about an individual's mental health in terms of any risk factors. For example, if somebody were to answer 'Not at all' it would be advisable to explore this issue in depth. The person may be thinking in the longer term, so a useful question may be:

– Can you set positive goals for today/tomorrow?

If it becomes clear that an individual is not able to see any future for themselves then the therapist will need to complete a detailed risk assessment.

Chapter Three

Worksheets

Sarah Mousley and Lucie Duncan

This chapter includes a series of worksheets developed to aid integration of the solution focused approach into occupational therapy practice. The sheets are all photocopiable. They are intended as an added resource to draw on when using the Solution Focused Measure of Occupational Function. There are worksheets that correspond to each question of the Measure, as well as a series of general worksheets.

There are three ways a worksheet can be used:

1. As part of the process of clarifying goals.
After completing the Measure the worksheets can help elicit important information that contributes to constructing solutions. For example, if someone was to answer 'sometimes' to question number 2, 'I have satisfying relationships', they could use the corresponding worksheet to work out exactly which relationships are working and why they work better than others. They could also gain insight into the qualities they possess that would help improve relationships in the future. Therefore using the worksheet may help analyse the qualities they possess and then enable them to work more on this area. Many of the worksheets could be considered a form of activity analysis which is carried out by the client.

2. As part of the process of working in more detail on a particular area chosen by the client (following the completion of the Measure).

For example, using the worksheet for question 7, 'Taking care of myself', will form the basis of an action plan by looking at exactly what the person wishes to achieve in this area of self care.

3. As homework.

It may become apparent during a session that further thought or work on a particular area would be useful. Completing a worksheet gives someone a structure to work with independently and bring to the next session.

The worksheets can be very useful because often people relate well to seeing something written down which they can then take away with them at the end of a session. It can be affirming as well as rewarding to complete a worksheet and see one's positive aspects in black and white.

As is often the case in solution focused work, an apparently simple task such as completing a worksheet may lead to awareness of strengths and resources that the person may have forgotten or neglected through a difficult period in their life. For someone who finds it hard to organise their thoughts being able to write something down may help to focus their thinking and overcome difficulties with concentration.

Zoe, aged 35, had lost confidence following a break in the relationship with her partner. She had become homeless and had been living on the streets for a number of months. By the time she met with the occupational therapist, she had just moved into a flat but was finding it extremely difficult to establish a routine. She identified this as an area she would like to work on. The occupational therapist gave her the worksheet for question 5, 'I can organise my week in a way that works me/satisfies me'. Zoe stated that she found using this particular worksheet extremely satisfying. By recording her existing weekly activities on the timetable, she could clearly see what she was already doing. This gave her the beginnings of a basic routine. It also highlighted where the gaps in her regular activities were and that most of her evenings were empty of arrangements.

Through discussion with the occupational therapist she was able to identify the evenings as the time in the day that she felt most lonely. Together they investigated clubs and activities that she could start attending with a friend. At a review, Zoe moved from 'sometimes' to 'mostly' on the Measure for 'satisfaction with time'.

She found the process of using the worksheet allowed her to visualise her week in a way that highlighted what she needed to do to feel more satisfied with her routine.

Using the worksheet as a homework task gives the client space to think something through in their own time.

Jamie, aged 24, was finding it hard to calm himself when feeling anxious. He was also feeling low and had withdrawn from his previously active work and social life. He believed that his problems started after he witnessed a suicide attempt by his father, along with a period of smoking large amounts of cannabis.

Jamie completed the Measure with the occupational therapist during two individual sessions. The occupational therapist asked questions to explore further how he wanted his life to look in the medium to longer term. The occupational therapist asked him to think about how he would know when it was time for him not to need the mental health services anymore. Jamie said that he needed more time to think about this as he could not come up with anything immediately. At the end of the session the occupational therapist asked Jamie if before the next session he could think over what they had discussed. The occupational therapist wrote down two questions for Jamie to take away with him (these appear as worksheet A). She asked him to write down his ideas as and when they came to him. The questions were:

"How will I (Jamie) know I am improving?"

"When will you (occupational therapist) know I am improving?"

A few days after this appointment, the occupational therapist was surprised to receive a number of neatly typed pages which Jamie had handed in to the receptionist when he attended another appointment at the mental health centre.

The occupational therapist was astounded to read Jamie's response to the questions she had asked him. There were 32 points to the first question and 13 to the second question. Examples of the responses he made to the first question were:

 - My interests and hobbies will grow, for example, more fishing, swimming and socialising
 - I would be able to deal with family disputes without feeling excessive stress and paranoia
 - I would make enquiries about part time work, send off applications and attend interviews. If I was able to cope with this I would then consider full-time employment to help fund a university course
 - I would spend less time in bed during the day and try to limit myself to eight hours at night (with a lie-in at weekends of course!)
 - I would learn to accept what has happened to me and regard it as a learning experience
 - A very important aspect to recovery - *I would be happy*

Some of the responses Jamie made to the second question about how the occupational therapist would know that he was improving were:

 - My sleep pattern would improve and earlier meetings could be arranged (maybe even 9.30 am but that would need very serious thought!)
 - You would find I may contribute more to the groups I attend, suggesting ideas and planning activities, as opposed to just attending and being a bystander, which I sometimes feel like
 - Finally when you visit, find me washed, clean shaven, bedroom tidy and I've at last bothered to get my CD player fixed, you know you will have done your job

These pages contained Jamie's own solutions in extraordinary detail and they also gave him and the occupational therapist some very clear goals to work towards. Jamie had painted a picture of how his life could be. This illustrated his ability to see a positive future for himself. Jamie had carried out an occupational analysis on his own life and had clearly linked satisfaction to occupational goals in a way that would have taken the occupational therapist many sessions to work out with Jamie had they focused only on verbal communication.

The occupational therapist had responded to Jamie's difficulty in formulating his thoughts within the session. Providing the worksheet seemed to have motivated Jamie to think about these issues in more depth and provided an easier format to express them in.

From what he had written, the occupational therapist and Jamie were able to prioritise the areas he wished to work on and devise an action plan bringing together Jamie's ideas and the occupational therapist's resources. At review Jamie's own solutions were used as a benchmark and each one was discussed and improvements were noted throughout.

Jamie's case was exceptional but serves as a reminder to us not to underestimate our clients and their ability to find their own solutions.

Guide to Worksheets

Worksheets A–H are general worksheets that can be used at any stage of collaboration. The remaining worksheets are linked to specific questions in the Solution Focused Measure of Occupational Function. There is no reason why the specific worksheets could not be used independently of the Measure if the opportunity arose. It is recommended that completed worksheets used as a starting point for a solution focused discussion as they tend to focus on exceptions, strengths or personal meanings of occupation.

A   Can be used with any question to further develop ideas and images of a future once a client has identified that they would like to improve in a particular area

B   Draws out exceptions

C   To elicit peoples' strengths and qualities from a first and third-person point of view

D   To draw out exceptions and strengths from the past that may be useful to the current situation

E   To help people identify their strengths and resources

F   To help people identify what is going well (exceptions) with their life right now. Developed from the 'formula first session task' *(de Shazer, 1985)*

G   To elicit a third-party view and consider how making changes might make a difference. Sometimes making changes leads to unexpected consequences or can upset others. Provides a chance to discuss this

H   This is a general worksheet to help develop self-esteem through the identification of achievements and skills. People become aware of their strengths and resources

Q1   Draws on exceptions to help people become aware of what is happening when they are comfortable talking to others

Q2   Draws on exceptions to help people become aware of what is happening when relationships work. Gives space for people to think about relationships they would like to improve and to visualise how they will recognise improvements

Q3   Elicits people's own meanings of confidence. Gives space for people to imagine what they would be like when they are confident

Q4   Draws on exceptions to help develop awareness of when and how people are managing to be assertive. Gives space to consider goals and identify small signs that they are beginning to achieve them

Q5   Draws on exceptions to help people link into their own decision-making skills in the past

Q6   Focuses on ways that people are satisfied with their home environment and changes they may like to make. Gives space to consider small steps towards creating a more satisfying home environment

Q7   Draws on exceptions to help people identify what they are doing at present to take care of themselves. Gives space to imagine what they will be doing when they become better at taking care of themselves when they have identified this as a desired change

Q8   Draws on exceptions to help people identify what they are doing at present to take care of the place where they live. Gives space to imagine what they will be doing when they become better at taking care of the place where they live when they have identified this as a desired change

Q9 A practical sheet to help people begin to manage their finances more effectively when this has been identified as a desired change

Q10 A practical sheet to help people develop a more satisfying weekly routine when they have identified this as a desired change

Q11 Helps to focus on the goals of being able to go out independently and identify benefits of doing this

Q12 Draws on exceptions to help people develop awareness of what they are doing to calm themselves. Gives space to imagine possible strategies they could use in the future. Gives space to set some small goals towards this

Q13 Draws on exceptions to help develop awareness of when and how people are managing their anger effectively. Gives space to consider goals and identify small signs they are beginning to achieve them

Q14 Draws on exceptions to help develop awareness of when and how people are managing to achieve what they set out to do. Gives space to consider goals and identify small signs they are beginning to achieve them

Q15 Draws on exceptions to help develop awareness of when and how people are managing to maintain their concentration. Gives space to consider the benefits that might ensue to increase motivation

Q16 Draws on exceptions from the recent and distant past to help people remember how they solve problems

Q17 Helps to identify activities and situations when people can see they are able to participate fully

Q18 Provides a weekly chart for people to record times when they have contributed to the needs of their family. This is intended to capture exceptions that may be missed as insignificant

Q19 Draws on exceptions that help to develop awareness of work skills. Provides space to consider current activities which may be occurring, not necessarily in a workplace, that show signs of work skills. Provides space for considering goals and resources

Q20 For people who would like to train or retrain in work but are uncertain of which direction to take. Draws on personal skills and values and also invites consideration of third-party opinions

Q21 Draws on people's own meanings of enjoyment and invites people to reconnect with memories of enjoyment. Introduces the idea of planning for enjoyment

Q22 For people who have identified a desire to take more exercise, this worksheet can stimulate motivation to carry this out

Q23 Draws on exceptions to help people develop awareness of what they are doing to help themselves get enough rest and sleep so they can do more of this

Q24 Draws on people's own meanings of support and understanding, considers present needs and how to achieve them

Q25 Stimulates ideas about changes that people would like to make in their lives. Gives space to imagine how they would recognise these changes happening. Can then be used to set positive goals for the future with people who find this difficult

Worksheet A

How will I know I am improving in the area of .... ?

What will I be doing differently?
What might others notice?
What will be happening?

What lets you know that you can succeed in achieving this goal?
Who in your life could be helpful to you in achieving this goal?

Worksheet B

Once you know what works, do more of it!
If it doesn't work, then don't do it again - do something different

What have you found that works for you?

Worksheet C

What are the strengths and qualities you possess that keep you going?

What would other people say your strengths and qualities are?

Worksheet D

When you faced this sort of situation in the past, how did you resolve it?

What skills or attributes did you use?

How could you do that again?

Worksheet E

I am resourceful

Positive experiences I have had

My Achievements

People I have to support me

My strengths and qualities

My skills and abilities

What I like about myself

Worksheet F

Between now and my next appointment I am going to notice and record the positive things that I want to continue happening in my life

Worksheet G

How will others see positive changes in me?

Person (e.g. friend, partner, relative)	What changes will they see in me?	How may it change our relationship?

Worksheet H

Self-Esteem

Write down all your achievements, however small, in the first column.
Next to each one write the skills it took to achieve it and any skills you learned/developed doing it.

Positive experiences I have had	My Achievements

Worksheet Q1

When do I feel comfortable talking to others?

What is different about these times?

What am I doing differently?

Worksheet Q2

My Relationships

■ The relationships in my life **that work** are with:	**■** What happens in these relationships that make them work?

■ The relationships **that I want to improve** are with:	**■** How will I know these relationships are improving?

Worksheet Q3

What does confidence mean to me?

3

How will I know I have confidence?

What will I be doing differently when I am confident?

Worksheet Q4

Assertiveness

The situations **I am able to be assertive are:**	What is happening when I am able to be assertive?

The situations **I would like to be more** assertive are:	How will I know when I am starting to achieve this?

Worksheet Q5

Making Decisions

Decisions I have made that I am proud of:	How did I make those decisions?

Worksheet Q6

Home Environment

I am satisfied with these aspects of my home environment:

I would like to change these aspects of my home environment:

I would like more of these aspects in my home environment:

What are the first small steps that I can take?

6

Worksheet Q7

Taking care of myself

I know I am taking care of myself because I...

7

I will know when I am taking better care of myself when I am...

Worksheet Q8

Taking care of the place where I live

I know I am taking care of the place where I live because I...

8

I will know when I am taking better care of the place where I live when I am...

Worksheet Q9

Managing my money

What do I have to spend my money on?

9

What do I like to spend my money on?

Worksheet Q10

My week plan

	Monday	Tuesday	Wednesday	Thursday	Friday	Saturday	Sunday
a.m.							
p.m.							
eve							

To feel more satisfied with my week I will be

A. Doing more of:

B. Doing less of:

C. Going to:

D. Seeing:

10

Getting to where I want and need to go

Where do I need to go?

Where do I want to be able to go?

11

What difference will it make to me to be able to get where I want/need to go?

Who or what could support me to get to where I want/need to go?

Worksheet Q12

Calming myself

The things I do now to help calm myself are:

....
....
....
....
....
....
....
....
....
....

I will feel more confident in my ability to calm myself when...

....
....
....
....
....
....
....
....
....
....

12

What I would like to try to do more of to help calm myself:

....
....
....
....
....
....
....
....
....
....

Worksheet Q13

Anger

When am I able to control my anger?	What am I doing that enables this to happen?

What am I doing instead of being angry?	How will I know when I am starting to achieve this?

Worksheet Q14

Achieving goals

**When am I able to achieve
what I set out to do, however small?**

**What am I doing
that enables this to happen?**

**How do I stay focused on
what I want to achieve?**

**What do I want to achieve
in the future?**

14

Concentration

What do I notice about the times when I am able to concentrate?

How can I make this happen more often?

15

What will I be doing more of when I am able to concentrate better?

Worksheet Q16

Problem solving

What problems, however small, have I managed to solve recently?

How did I do this?

What is the biggest problem I have ever solved?

How did I do that?

Worksheet Q17

Think about the times when you are absorbed in what you are doing...

What am I doing? (list as many activities as you want and answer tthe questions for each one)	Where am I?	Who else is around?	What are they doing?

17

Worksheet Q18

Meeting the needs of my family

Before you go to sleep each night write down anything you did, however small, towards meeting the needs of people in your family.

Monday	Tuesday	Wednesday	Thursday	Friday	Saturday	Sunday

18

Worksheet Q19

Work skills

What do I do when I function well at work?

What aspects of this am I doing at the moment?

What small steps could I take to improve this?

Who or what can help me?

Worksheet Q20

What do I want to do?

What was I good at at school?

What do I enjoy doing?

What am I good at?

What am I passionate about?

What's important to me?

20

What do other people value about me?

Worksheet Q21

Enjoyment

How do I know when I'm enjoying myself?

When was the last time I noticed I was enjoying myself?

What am I doing when I am enjoying myself?

When was the last time I planned an activity to enjoy myself?

21

Worksheet Q22

Exercise

What benefits will I notice when I take regular exercise?

What will I be doing differently when I am taking regular exercise?

What will other people notice about me?

Who could support me to maintain regular exercise?

Rest and sleep

What am I doing differently when I get enough rest and sleep?

How am I helping this happen?

How can I do more of this?

23

Worksheet Q24

Support and understanding

When have I felt supported and understood even in a small way?

What difference did this make?

What support and understanding do I need now?

What small step could I take towards achieving this?

Worksheet Q25

Making changes

The changes I want to make in my life are:	How will I know these changes are beginning to happen?

CHAPTER FOUR

CONTINUING PROFESSIONAL DEVELOPMENT

Lucie Duncan and Sarah Mousley

Continuing professional development (CPD) is an essential require-
ment for all health professionals. It has been described by the
Department of Health as: 'Lifelong learning; improving and maintaining
the quality of practice; facilitating changes in practice and expanding
competencies' *(DOH, 2003)*. It is so highly valued that practitioners will
have to demonstrate that they have undertaken CPD activities in order
to keep their professional registration.

An important aspect of CPD is reflection. The aim is to continu-
ally review one's own practice and identify learning needs, interests and
goals. Most health professionals are now expected to have a development
plan which includes both professional practice and career aims. There is
now a blossoming of literature about the reflective process, and models
of reflective practice provide useful guidelines on how to engage with
this important skill.

There are two sets of worksheets in this chapter. The first set, 'Who
Am I?', provides a focus and structure for personal reflection and can
offer valuable insight into how you are functioning as an occupational

therapist. The second set, 'Turning Points', focuses on reflection on professional practice and allows you to learn from important events and reflect on your journey as an occupational therapist. There are explanations of each set of worksheets at the beginning of the sections.

Section One: Who Am I?

The 'Who Am I?' reflective process contains the following worksheets:

- − 'Who Am I?' preparation exercise
- − 'Who Am I?' personal reflections sheet
- − Goal-setting sheet
- − Ongoing reflection sheets

1. 'Who Am I?' preparation exercise

This exercise is based on 15 qualities which are selected from the National Health Service benchmark statements as representing best practice in occupational therapy (these can be viewed at *www.qaa.ac.uk*). You may like to expand or adapt this list to make it more individual to you.

Each quality is accompanied by a 10-point scale followed by two questions. The questions should draw out your strengths and achievements and suggest areas for improvement.

The sheet is designed to be used yearly as a self-assessment and may usefully be carried out before an appraisal. You can also give the sheet to your colleagues and/or service user to be completed by them to provide feedback about your performance. Because the questions are designed to draw out what is working well, feedback is more likely to be compliments.

2. 'Who Am I?' personal reflections sheet

After completing the preparation sheet and/or receiving a completed preparation sheet from a colleague and/or service user, you should use this sheet to reflect on the information gained. This process allows a certain detachment from the initial reflections and acts as a bridge between them and future goals.

3. 'Who Am I?' goal-setting sheet

To draw all this information together there is a goal-setting sheet which can be used as a personal development tool or as a preparation for appraisal. Following the blank copy there is an example of a completed sheet.

4. 'Who Am I?' ongoing reflections sheet

Finally, this last sheet helps you to keep an ongoing log in order to maintain and develop your professional self-awareness. This can also form the basis of preparation for supervision.

1 Ability to listen

0	5	10

What am I already doing? ....
....
....
....
....

What do I need to do more of? ....
....
....

2 Ability to communicate

0	5	10

What am I already doing? ....
....
....
....
....

What do I need to do more of? ....
....
....

3 Approachability/getting rapport

0	5	10

What am I already doing? ....
....
....
....
....

What do I need to do more of? ....
....
....

4 Harnessing motivation

0	5	10

What am I already doing? ....
....
....
....
....

What do I need to do more of? ....
....
....

5 Time management

0	5	10

What am I already doing? ....
....
....
....
....

What do I need to do more of? ....
....
....

6 Ability to show empathy

0	5	10

What am I already doing? ....
....
....
....
....

What do I need to do more of? ....
....
....

7 Finding original creative solutions

0	5	10

What am I already doing?

....

....

....

....

What do I need to do more of?

....

....

8 Self reflection

0	5	10

What am I already doing?

....

....

....

....

What do I need to do more of?

....

....

9 Planning skills

0	5	10

What am I already doing?

....

....

....

....

What do I need to do more of?

....

....

10 Responsibility for professional development

0	5	10

What am I already doing? ....
....
....
....
....

What do I need to do more of? ....
....
....

11 Reasoning/problem solving

0	5	10

What am I already doing? ....
....
....
....
....

What do I need to do more of? ....
....
....

12 Ability to prioritise

0	5	10

What am I already doing? ....
....
....
....
....

What do I need to do more of? ....
....
....

13 Being an advocate

0	5	10

What am I already doing?

....

....

....

....

What do I need to do more of?

....

....

14 Leadership

0	5	10

What am I already doing?

....

....

....

....

....

What do I need to do more of?

....

....

15 Assertiveness

0	5	10

What am I already doing?

....

....

....

....

....

What do I need to do more of?

....

....

What have learned about myself?

What surprised me?

Positive things to build on

What would I like to develop?

How will I know that I have reached a point I am satisfied with?

How do I hope the responses to this exercise will be different in six months?

What I would like to achieve in the next year at work?

How will I know when I have been successful?

How will my clients and/or colleagues know?

What am I already doing in order to achieve this goal?

What skills and personal qualities do I have that will help me achieve this goal?

What will I be doing differently/more of in order to achieve this goal?

What resources are available to me? e.g. training, colleagues

Where am I at the moment?

| 0 | 5 | 10 |

Where do I want to be?

| 0 | 5 | 10 |

By when?

What are the first steps I need to take?

What I would like to achieve in the next year at work?

To manage my workload and stress levels

How will I know when I have been successful?

I will be happier, and want to go to work
My sense of humour will return
I will be calmer
Will feel in control

How will my clients and/or colleagues know?

I will be more patient and fun to be around

What am I already doing in order to achieve this goal?

Using supervision
Started yoga
Discussing issues with colleagues
Trying to prioritise my work

What skills and personal qualities do I have that will help me achieve this goal?

I can think logically
I normally stick at something until I've done it
I am organised
I am good at asking for help when I need it

What will I be doing differently/more of in order to achieve this goal?

I need to clearly identify where my stress is coming from
I need to spend more time looking at my role and responsibilities when prioritising my work
Prioritise work on weekly basis - write lists and check they are realistic

What resources are available to me? e.g. training, colleagues

In-house training for stress and time management
Supervision
Talk to other OTs

Where am I at the moment?

```
0                    5                    10
```

Where do I want to be?

```
0                    5                    10
```

By when? 2 months time

What are the first steps I need to take?

Sit and brainstorm where main stressors are arising
Arrange supervision to discuss these issues and seek advice from manager
Get organised! Start weekly to-do list

Date ....

▉ Experience

....
....

▉ Satisfaction with performance

0	5	10

▉ What I did that worked, and how did I know this? i.e. my attitude, preparation

....
....
....

▉ What I learned about myself

....
....
....

▉ What I would like to differently next time

....
....
....

▉ How will my clients and/or colleagues know that I am applying this more consistently?

....
....
....

▉ What is the next small step I need to take to feel more satisfied in this area?

....
....
....

Section Two: Turning Points

This set of worksheets provides an opportunity to identify and reflect on 'turning points' that have occurred during your work. They may be positive situations and achievements you have made or something more difficult such as a crisis or a traumatic event. There is no right or wrong way to use this exercise – it is purely for personal reflection and can be used to highlight particular milestones in your work experience. Unlike other exercises you may have done previously, this one may help you identify situations other than academic or work achievements.

The first 'Turning Points' worksheet, 'My work journey so far', can be used to record these events/situations in chronological order, like a journey. Once they have been recorded, the 'Turning Points prompt questions' will help to elicit what you gained from your turning points. You may like to choose one or more of your turning points and run through a few of the prompt questions.

On the following pages you will find blank copies of the 'Turning Points' worksheets followed by examples of completed ones to give an idea of how they work.

Turning Points
My work journey so far

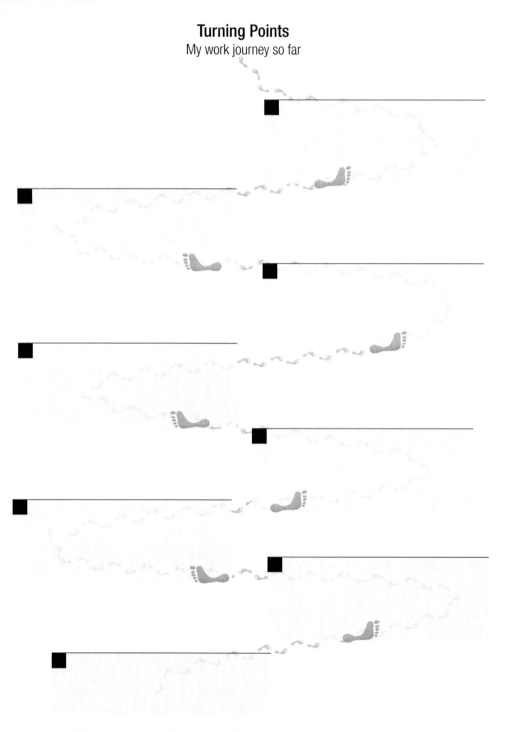

You can use all or only some of these prompts as headings to expand on your Turning Points journey

What I learned about myself

What skills I developed

What I took from this event to be more effective in the future

Biggest achievements

Contacts I made

People who inspired me

Resources I develop or enjoyed using/found useful

How I coped with the challenges

Turning Points

My work journey so far

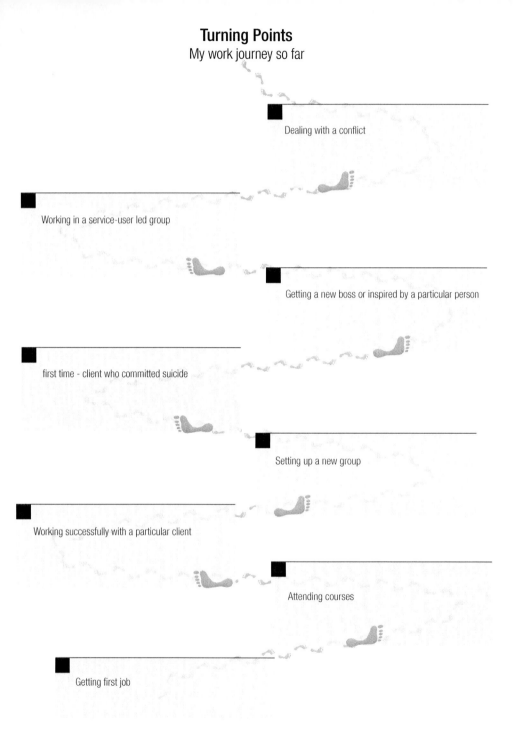

Dealing with a conflict

Working in a service-user led group

Getting a new boss or inspired by a particular person

first time - client who committed suicide

Setting up a new group

Working successfully with a particular client

Attending courses

Getting first job

Setting up a new group

What I learned about myself

A greater knowledge about the subject of the group (communication, skills)
Better time management
An ability to negotiate with my co-facilitator
Increased organisational ability
Creative ideas for activities within the group

Resources I develop or enjoyed using/found useful

Liaising with speech therapist - got to understand her role better and enjoyed getting to know her
Discovered new books
Gained a useful resource pack of communication skills activities

What I took from this event to be more effective in the future

An increased sense of confidence in my own abilities
An awareness of my strengths and limitations in group facilitation
Ability to constructively analyse the group format and make changes for next time

First time a client committed suicide

What I learned about myself

Ability to ask others for support
Not afraid to think about what I could have done differently
My intuition can be trusted
I can be calm in a crisis

How I coped with the challenge

Talked to colleagues who had experience-learnt from them and sought reassurance
Let myself be upset
Took time to review what I knew- remembering its always easier in hindsight
Wrote a poem about the person

What I took from this event to be more effective in the future

Take notice of intuitive feelings
Realising the importance of risk assessment
Realising that I can't control other people
Realising that people may not always tell you everything- may just tell you what they think you want to hear
    (service user and family)
Importance of accurate note-taking

Section Three: Supervision

Clinical supervision is an important part of maintaining a safe and accountable professional practice. Clinical supervision within the National Health Service is described as 'a formal process of professional support and learning which enables individual practitioners to develop knowledge and competence, assume responsibility for their own practice and enhance consumer protection and safety of care in complex clinical situations' *(DOH, 1993)*.

Supervision is also an important part of continuing professional development and should provide an opportunity for clinicians to reflect on their practice and continue to develop professional self-awareness. Clinical supervision tends to take the form of a senior member of staff supervising a junior member of staff and therefore may reflect the therapeutic style of the senior staff member or of the unit, if there is an established procedure. As such, the supervision method will be likely to be problem-focused whereby difficulties or problem cases are brought for discussion.

We would like to offer some thoughts regarding a more solution focused approach to supervision. Therapists familiar with a solution focused approach will find this supervision style useful to their practice. If the therapist is working in a solution focused way, then solution focused supervision will be most helpful to them. However, we feel that even when working with therapists using a problem-focused approach, solution focused supervision can work effectively. This is because in all solution focused work, the 'client' is regarded as holding the expertise of their own situation. So, if supervising a therapist who favours a cognitive behavioural approach, solution focused supervision should empower them to examine the strengths of their approach and build on that, rather than attempting to compete with or guide the supervisee into a different approach.

In the following pages we offer some ideas for enhancing the supervision process through using a solution focused approach.

Establishing an atmosphere of competence

Establishing a rapport with your supervisee is just as important as establishing a rapport with clients. Supervision will be more comfortable and useful if the supervisee feels acknowledged and appreciated and senses that you have confidence in their abilities. They will also begin to appreciate their own qualities and skills and feel confidence in using them if they are focused on in supervision.

For this reason it is useful to start supervision with a request for examples of success. How these were achieved should be explored in some detail.

The Brief Therapy Practice has provided some useful questions:
— Describe a piece of work that you did in the recent past that you are proud of
— How did you do that?
— What qualities and skills were required to make that happen?
— How did you do that?
— Who noticed?
— What did they notice?

As you can see, the supervisor is essentially engaging in strengths-based questioning, starting with the assumption that the supervisee will produce an example of good work. The questions build up a picture of the supervisee's competence through individual and third-party views.

Personal Development Goal-Setting

For the supervisee, the fact that their supervisor knows and recognises their goals is very supportive. To identify goals some of the following questions will be useful:
— What do you hope to achieve in the next (x) months?
— When you are performing at your next level of ability, what will you be doing differently?
— What characteristics will you have?
— What new skills will you have learned or be developing?
— Is there anyone who can help you to achieve your goal?
— What progress would you like to notice happening between now and our next meeting?

Caseload Supervision

The supervisee will usually want to discuss cases in which they would like support and guidance. The following are some ideas of how to discuss cases.

The Miracle Question

Bill O'Connell has written about the use of the Miracle Question in supervision. He states that asking this question can encourage the supervisee to talk about their practice without feeling they have to defend or justify themselves.

Example: "If you were working better with this client and your current difficulties have been overcome, what would be the first signs for you that a miracle has happened?" *(O'Connell, 1998).*

We have used this question and variations of it and found it very informative and revealing. It can open up new avenues for exploration and discussion.

Clarifying Client's Goals

There are also some general questions that can be asked:
- What does the client want to change or want help with?
- What would the client like to change about this?
- So what does the client want to be doing instead?
- If the client were on-track to (making this decision, solving this problem) what might he/she say they would be doing differently?
- What would you be doing differently?
- How will you know that things have improved for your client?
- What client behaviours will indicate to you that this problem is on-track to being solved?
- Is that what the client says he/she wants?

Future Oriented Questions

This style of questioning is useful when a supervisee is feeling 'stuck' working with someone for whom problems do not appear to be resolving. By asking the supervisee to describe the situation when the problem is not there or what the future will look like without the problem, they will have begun to describe the solution.

- How will you know when 'x' has resolved their situation? What will be happening differently?
- What would be happening in your work with 'x' for you to realise that you do not feel stuck anymore?
- What will be the first small sign that lets you know that things are moving forwards?

Scaling

Scaling questions in supervision can generate useful discussion, and are also useful for measuring progress. In addition they can help the supervisee see where they stand with a particular case and may offer valuable insights into the individual's feelings and attitudes. Through discussion, the resources and skills of the supervisee can be drawn out. Some examples of how scaling questions can be used and adapted in supervision are as follows:

- If 0 represents the time that this case was taken on and 10 represents a time when you believe 'x' no longer needs to see you, where do you see yourself at the present time?
- How do you know you are at this point?
- What will be happening when you have moved on one point?
- Where on this scale will represent good enough for you/'x'?
- How will you know when you have got there?
- If 0 represents that you believe change is not possible in this piece of work and 10 represents your total confidence of a successful outcome, where do you see yourself now?
- What would be happening for your confidence in change to have moved on one point?

Exceptions

Using questions that explore exceptions can help focus on the positive aspects of difficult situations. This can be particularly useful in situations that feel to the supervisee as though they are not changing or moving forward. Responses to these questions can often lead directly to workable solutions. Exception questions may look like this:

- Are there any times when you feel less frustrated with your work with 'x'?
- What do you notice about those times? What is happening at those times?
- When is 'x' doing some of what he/she wants to do in relation to the problem?
- When is 'x' feeling they are making progress towards achieving their goals?
- Are there times when you would expect difficulties to occur for 'x', and they don't occur? What would you say was different about those times?

Exception questions can also be applied more generally to any work issue.

Compliments

Supervision can be more comfortable and productive when the supervisee feels acknowledged, appreciated and senses that you have confidence in their abilities. Compliments can also highlight positive trends. Some examples are:

- I'm impressed with the way you handled that situation. You showed a lot of …
- How did you do that?
- That situation sounded very challenging. You needed a lot of … to resolve it.
- When else have you used this strategy? Is it something you could develop further?

Positive feedback should include any observations regarding a person's skills, strengths and positive qualities. Supervision can be linked to continuing professional development through the worksheets and tools introduced at the beginning of this chapter.

Self-Reflection

Finally, here are some question that can be used as a reflective tool at the end of a session or while reviewing a case:

- Do I know what the person's goals of therapy are?
- Have I identified exceptions to when the problem is happening?
- Do I know where on the scale the person is now?
- Do I know what the person's strengths and resources are?
- Do I know what the persons coping strategies are?
- Do I know how they have survived so far?
- Do I know what the next small step is for the person?
- What compliments have I paid to the person?
- Do I know what I have done that the person has found useful?
- On a scale of 0–10 where 10 is total satisfaction with how this work with the person is going, where do I rate myself? How do I know?
- What can I do differently next time to reach the next point on my scale?

CHAPTER FIVE

EXAMPLES FROM PRACTICE

Lucie Duncan, Rayya Ghul, Sarah Mousley

In order to give a flavour of the type of conversations that an occupational therapist can engage in when using the Solution Focused Measure of Occupational Function we have included transcripts of three interviews.

We have chosen clients who are similar to those most occupational therapists working in mental health services might come across. The first, Colin, a man with long-term mental health difficulties, had withdrawn from the outside world and although known to local services, was considered hard to engage with. We chose Colin because the interview gives good examples of how the Measure can generate exceptions - times when the problem is not present or is happening less. The second, Becky, is a young single mother who became depressed following the removal of her baby for adoption. In this interview the occupational therapist used the Measure to produce a preferred future and used the categories from 'not at all' to 'definitely' as a scale. Both of these transcripts are selections from the complete initial interview.

The third client, John, is a young man who had become unstable after smoking cannabis and found himself on an acute in-patient unit.

This was John's first admission and he was frightened that he would never be able to regain his life. This transcript is much longer and covers most of the interview. We decided to include it because it gives a good sense of how the occupational therapist used the Measure to draw out John's strengths and resources and create hope and optimism for the future. It also shows how interventions that link into a client's occupational identity and skills can quickly be generated from the information provided. This means that the client is more likely to be motivated to engage with an occupational therapy programme.

The 'Weirdo' Next Door

Most occupational therapists working in the community will know someone like Colin; a man with a diagnosis of schizophrenia, living alone, increasingly neglecting his self-care and care of his home. His appearance and sometimes odd behaviour have been noticed by his neighbours, who at best ignore and avoid him and at worst bully and harass him. The services he is involved with often do not see further than his diagnosis and their low expectations for his future. What the occupational therapist does in the following case study is not radical and is not that different to what any community occupational therapist might offer. What may be of interest to the reader is the speed with which his underlying story was uncovered and some of the ways the Measure was used to generate further detail.

Colin was referred to the community occupational therapist by the community psychiatric nurse, who was concerned that Colin might be neglecting himself and his house.

He was in his 40s and lived alone in a house he owned. He was known to mental health services as having long-term mental health difficulties with a dominant symptom of hearing voices which at times could disturb and distress him. In the past he had had three admissions to an acute in-patient unit. The information the service had about Colin was that he was often hostile to people, especially his neighbours, that he only ate fried food and that his house was so severely neglected that environmental health intervention was being considered. He was considered to have little or no skills in activities of daily living.

Initially Colin would not let the occupational therapist into the house when she tried to undertake a home visit. Eventually he allowed her in when she jokingly said that he might as well get her visit 'over and done with' because she would keep coming back until he let her in. When the occupational therapist entered the house the neglect was evident. There was also evidence of deliberate abuse to the fabric of the house. The curtains were drawn and there was a strong smell of cigarette smoke. When the therapist sat down she became aware of a 'pyramid' of cigarette ash just below the arm of the armchair. It was obvious that Colin spent a lot of his time sitting in the chair smoking.

The occupational therapist, who at that time also smoked, asked if she could light up. She did so and without comment proceeded to flick her ash onto the pyramid. At this, Colin appeared to relax somewhat and asked the occupational therapist what she wanted. She explained that people were concerned about his well-being and that she had been asked to visit. After a small discussion, Colin agreed to the occupational therapist interviewing him using the Measure.

Questions 1 and 2 were answered and revealed that Colin was happy to talk to people when they did not think they knew everything about him 'like the nurses on the ward', and that he had only one friend, called Tony, whom he saw occasionally and liked because he put no pressure on Colin. He had met Tony while in hospital and they had kept in contact after being discharged.

Questions 3 and 4 will be transcribed in detail as they gave rise to a huge amount of information that had not been known to the services even after three admissions.

THERAPIST: OK, the next statement is 'I have confidence in myself'.

COLIN: *(long pause)* I think I used to. I used to have confidence in myself.

THERAPIST: So what was different when you used to have confidence in yourself?

COLIN: I used to manage things well... didn't have to think about things. I used to manage the house after

Mum died.

THERAPIST: How long ago did your Mum die?

COLIN: My Mum died eight years ago and then it was just me and my brother.

THERAPIST: And where is your brother now?

COLIN: He died four years ago. He was ill for a while and couldn't look after himself... He was disabled.

THERAPIST: How did the two of you manage then?

COLIN: I used to do everything for him... I looked after him until he died.

THERAPIST: Gosh, that must have been a difficult time, how did you manage?

COLIN: Wasn't difficult, I've always looked after my brother. He had a learning disability and after Mum died I did everything, I used to do everything for him.

THERAPIST: What sort of things did you do?

COLIN: You know, helped him wash and dress, cooked for him, took him to the Day Centre... you know... he had to go to a Day Centre... and then I would pick him up.

THERAPIST: What sort of things did you cook in those days?

COLIN: Everything. Anything.

THERAPIST: Can you give me some examples?

COLIN: Oh you know... shepherd's pie, steak and kidney pie, chops, vegetables... all from fresh, didn't use any of that pre-packaged stuff.

THERAPIST: Wow, that's pretty impressive.

COLIN: No it's not, it had to be done so I did it.

THERAPIST: Where did you learn to cook?

COLIN: From Mum, but I used to create some of my own dishes too, for a bit of variety. But it's no fun just cooking for one.

THERAPIST: So did you take care of the house too?

COLIN: Yes, I did the washing and cleaning... everything after Mum died.

THERAPIST: That's quite something you did for your brother, was it hard?

COLIN: No, it was easy... it was easy because it had to be done. Nothing special, it had to be done. He had to be taken care of, he was my brother. I had a reason to do it all. Now there's no reason to do it, now that it's only me.

THERAPIST: You obviously had a lot of skills – you were good at doing a lot of things.

COLIN: I suppose so, I didn't think about it, I just did it.

THERAPIST: So where would you put yourself now in terms of your confidence?

COLIN: Well, I know I could do it even though everyone thinks I can't.

THERAPIST: So... ?

COLIN: ...Mostly?

THERAPIST: *(puts cross in box)* Mostly. *(pause)*... so what would be different if you were moving up to definitely then?

COLIN: I suppose I'd show myself that I could do it again.

THERAPIST: Can I ask you, then, how did you manage it all when you were also hearing voices?

COLIN: The voices didn't bother me so much then, when I was looking after him, I didn't have time for them, things had to be done.

THERAPIST: OK, let's take a look at the next question, 'I can stand up for myself.'

COLIN: I stood up for my brother, especially when he was being teased by the idiots around here. They're so ignorant, making fun of someone just because he's different, idiots. They wanted to take him away, put him in a home. I fought that. I wasn't going to let him go in a home, his home was here and it was my job to look after him after Mum died. I didn't like the idea of him being looked after by someone else... I think people think I'm aggressive... I do

get angry with people… they don't take time to
understand me, it makes me angry.

THERAPIST: So if people did take the time, what would they see
instead?

COLIN: They wouldn't see me in such a hopeless light, just
a schizophrenic. I think they'd see I have some
skills, that they don't have to worry about me… all
the time, anyway. Like they always do, hounding
me and visiting me every five minutes, sending in
people like you to check up on me.

THERAPIST: *(laughs)* So what do you think you'll be doing when
people stop hounding you?

COLIN: I'd enjoy the peace and quiet, just get on with my
life… but I suppose I'd still be a bit fed up… maybe
I need to get out a bit.

THERAPIST: Well, you did say that one of the things you liked
about Tony was that he got you out of the house…
that he sometimes had to 'drag' you out. Perhaps
it's just the way people hound you that makes the
difference?

These two questions revealed a lot about Colin. He was clearly a capable
and compassionate individual whose life had lost meaning after he lost his
roles and occupations following the death of his mother and brother. He
was annoyed by the attitude, as he perceived it, of the professionals he'd
met who had not bothered to find out any of this but had approached
him with the assumption that he was incapable and always had been.
We are also beginning to see an exception providing a chink in his
desire to stay indoors and be left alone. He has admitted that he likes it
when his friend drags him out to the pub and thinks he could get out
a bit more.

The next questions revealed more about Colin:

THERAPIST: Right then, 'I am able to make decisions when I
need to.'

COLIN: Well, I don't really need to make decisions about
anything… it's a long time since I had to make

decisions… I used to make decisions all the time, you know what to make us to eat in the week, when to do things, what clothes my brother needed…

THERAPIST: Are there any small decisions you make now?

COLIN: Whether to take my medication or not… which I wonder about. And I didn't before I went into hospital. The nurses seem to think it helps me. My Mum always used to give me my medication and I still took it after she died… I kind of thought it would help me look after my brother. I suppose I've made that decision – to take it now, I don't know why… there's only me.

THERAPIST: What else?

COLIN: I like listening to the radio. I suppose I choose the stations I like to listen to. I like classical music. But I suppose I don't do a lot else really. I smoke and listen to the radio, eat the same thing every day – bacon sandwiches. The nurses think that's bad, that's why they sent you round, they think I'm going to have a heart attack.

THERAPIST: The next question is, 'I am satisfied with my home environment.'

COLIN: Yes I am, definitely. It's cosy, it's all I need… well, I'd like to get that window mended. I've always lived here, with my Mum and my brother. It's full of memories. I don't go upstairs any more. I sleep here in the armchair. Upstairs is a bit of a state.

THERAPIST: Are you happy sleeping in the armchair?

COLIN: Yeah… sometimes I get a bit stiff. But my radio's here and I can turn it up when my voices get worse. There's too much stuff upstairs… I might want to sleep up there but all my Mum's things are up there. I think some of it needs to be moved.

THERAPIST: Do you want to move it?

COLIN: I don't really know how to, there's too much stuff. It's the way it was when they were around and I don't really want to throw things away. I don't need to go upstairs anyway, I've got everything I need down here, I can smoke and sit in the armchair.

THERAPIST: Yes, you do seem to have a comfortable life. OK... 'I can take care of myself'...

COLIN: I think so... I worry about these stains on my fingers, I suppose it's because I smoke too much, I need to get these stains off my fingers. I can cook for myself. I don't clean the house as you can see. They said they want to send in a helper.

THERAPIST: You don't fancy that?

COLIN: I don't want someone interfering... but I'm OK. I don't go into the garden much, because the children throw stones.

THERAPIST: What, the neighbours?

COLIN: All the local children, they throw stones at me in the garden. I don't talk to the neighbours. They complain about me. They want me to go into hospital. They thought I was doing strange things in the garden.

THERAPIST: Were you?

COLIN: No. I had rubbish collecting... it may have been a bit dirty, a bit smelly. It builds up you know... I might have had the radio a bit loud... I have to turn it up when the voices get bad, to distract me sometimes.

THERAPIST: You do strike me as a very independent person; you don't like people interfering in your life.

COLIN: Yes, I don't really like people.

THERAPIST: You like Tony though.

COLIN: Yes, I like Tony.

These questions tended to elicit some of the realities of Colin's life. He spends his time doing very little. He is also subject to a lot of harassment from other people, particularly his neighbours, although he has a little insight into what he might be doing to attract it. However, this is a common story heard from people living with voices and other disturbing symptoms which sometimes lead to bizarre behaviour; other people in their community do not understand them, stigmatise them and behave in a hostile manner. As the occupational therapist continued through the Measure, many of the questions elicited no real answer other than 'I don't because I don't do a lot', and also revealed a deep-seated suspicion of other people, which was quite understandable. However, question 10 gave rise to an exception which within the week would form a stepping-stone for Colin to begin to regain some occupations and roles.

THERAPIST: So, can you organise your week in a way that works for you or satisfies you?

COLIN: Well, I just smoke really. *(pause)* I suppose it would be nice to do a few more things.

THERAPIST: What kind of things would you like to do?

COLIN: Not what you lot want to make me do – send people round to take me shopping to buy healthy food. It doesn't really interest me. I suppose I like going to the pub. Maybe… they tell me you do some groups.

THERAPIST: Yes.

COLIN: Maybe I could go to one of them. Maybe I'd meet someone like Tony who I'd like. Tony goes to a group, a discussion group. I don't think I fancy talking though. Some of your crafty things, I suppose I could give them a try. Might keep you lot quiet anyway. Keep you off my back *(laughs)*.

THERAPIST: Have you done craft-type things before?

COLIN: No, well I did things… I did a bit of carpentry… I did things around the house for Mum. I did odd jobs for people. I can do most things.

THERAPIST: You can come and give us a hand! We've just started a furniture restoration group and it seemed like a good idea at the time, but we are struggling a bit... with knowing exactly how to do some of the woodwork.

COLIN: Have you got all the tools that you need?

THERAPIST: I don't honestly know if we've got all the right tools – we did have some help from someone but...

COLIN: You really should know what you're doing when you're teaching that kind of thing.

THERAPIST: Well, I think you're right.

COLIN: Because it can be quite dangerous with tools. Who does it? Do you do it?

THERAPIST: Yes, me and someone else.

COLIN: I'd be happy to come along and see what you're doing.

THERAPIST: That would be great – I mean we do the bits we know are safe, but I'm sure there's a lot more that we could be doing if we had someone who knew what they were doing.

COLIN: Yeah, I'd come along and help.

THERAPIST: We'd really appreciate that.

COLIN: Can I smoke there?

THERAPIST: Yes, there's a smoking area.

This exception is built on in question 20:

THERAPIST: Would you like to be able to work or to do some training to work?

COLIN: I don't think anyone would want to employ me. I did used to enjoy working a bit.

THERAPIST: Did you? What did you do?

COLIN: I did some carpentry, you know earning a bit of cash.

THERAPIST: Oh yes, you mentioned that. What did you like about it?

COLIN: Umm... working with wood... it was nice, I was quite good at the things I did... It got me out of the house I suppose, gave me time out of the house away from my mother and brother…

THERAPIST: So is doing some kind of work something you might consider in the future?

COLIN: I suppose if anyone would have me, I would, but I don't think there would be anywhere that would want someone with schizophrenia. I'd have to be able to smoke while I was there, and most places don't let you do that now.

THERAPIST: That's right. Well, we could certainly look into it. If it was something you were interested in, it's something that I can look into, I can't give you any promises, but it is part of my job – there are various schemes that are running to help people like yourself.

COLIN: Well, if someone would take me on and see if I'm up to it, I'd give it a try. *(pause)* I find it hard to get up in the morning. I don't get up till one in the afternoon.

THERAPIST: Well, you can do it bit by bit – get used to it, you don't have to do it all at once.

Aside from this, as mentioned earlier, Colin's responses to other questions largely indicated that he did very little. When the occupational therapist reached the end of the interview, it seems that Colin was ready to consider making some changes:

THERAPIST: We're nearly at the end now, the next question is 'I have people who understand and support me.'

COLIN: I think Tony understands me… because we've similar problems, with voices and things. But apart from that I don't really have anyone… so 'sometimes'.

THERAPIST: Is that something you'd like to see moving up towards mostly or definitely?

COLIN: Yes I think I would. It gets a bit lonely. I don't talk to people.

THERAPIST: So if was at 'mostly' what difference would that

make to you?

COLIN: I suppose I could just get away from sitting here in my own thoughts, do a bit more, talk to people more.

THERAPIST: What difference would that make?

COLIN: I suppose I would get out a bit more. I get a bit fed up sometimes, you know being in here all the time... it might be nice to make some friends, get a bit of support.

THERAPIST: And you could give support to others – you mentioned earlier that you liked it when you could help Tony.

COLIN: Yes that's true.

THERAPIST: Right – last question! 'I can make positive goals for the future.'

COLIN: I don't really think about the future. I find it hard to plan... I don't really plan or think about things.

THERAPIST: Is that something you'd like to be able to do?

COLIN: Yes... when I... I have had plans to do this place, try and be a bit cleaner.

THERAPIST: So if you had a small goal for the future, what might that be?

COLIN: *(pause)* I suppose I'd like to get out more.

Following this interview, the occupational therapist gave the following feedback and compliments and then moved into setting some more concrete goals:

THERAPIST: Thank you very much for taking the time to talk to me, it's been enormously helpful – I hope it wasn't as bad as you thought it was going to be.

COLIN: No it's been OK I suppose *(laughs)*.

THERAPIST: I'm so impressed by what you told me about your brother. I mean I know you said that it was something you had to do, but there are a lot of people who might not have done that – they might have a relative and decide to put them in a home, but you actually fought to keep him at home. So you did carry out your duty and it sounds like you did it well.

And I'm thinking about the fact that you do seem to be someone who likes to help people. Also, you do have a lot of skills, practical skills, and although you don't seem to be using them at the moment, they are there.

COLIN: Yeah I guess so, it's just that I've not thought it worth using them when it's just me. I suppose I'm a bit fed up really.

THERAPIST: OK, I've told you a few bits and pieces about what we offer in the Day Service, but I was wondering if there were changes you'd like to see happening?

COLIN: Well I'd like to come along to one of those groups – that furniture one. When is it?

THERAPIST: It's in the morning.

COLIN: Well, it might be OK. Could you come and get me? I don't want to be walking down on my own.

THERAPIST: Well, I could at first – certainly until you got into the routine of it. If you think that would help.

COLIN: Will you be there? In the group?

THERAPIST: Yes I will.

COLIN: OK I'll give it a try.

Outcome

Colin agreed to give the furniture restoration group a try and slowly began to attend regularly. The occupational therapist agreed to pick him up for a couple of weeks and walk with him until he felt confident to walk to the service on his own. Colin turned out to be skilled in woodwork techniques and it was obvious that he found pleasure in helping other group members with their chosen projects. His sense of humour also started becoming more evident and often took the form of gentle mocking of the two occupational therapists' lack of knowledge and skill.

Once his routine in attending the furniture restoration group became more established and he was familiar with the other members and became more relaxed with the rest of the service staff, he began attending two additional groups at the day service. He reported that he felt happier as he was getting out of the house and was feeling better about himself. At the service he also made another friend whom he occasionally met at a local café.

After six months the occupational therapist was able to introduce Colin to Shaw Trust (a local employment project). A suitable local work placement was found in a carpenter's business and a plan was made with Colin for him to work voluntarily for one morning a week. As he was quite anxious, he asked that the occupational therapist initially go with him and this was arranged. As before, he soon developed the confidence to walk to his job alone. He was surprised at how welcoming the staff were toward him and slowly began to feel more sure of himself around other people. He was pleased to have the opportunity to prove to himself that he could be productive and work alongside others again.

'A Vase on the Table'

Occupational therapists often find themselves working in complex situations with people whose mental distress is intertwined with the difficult circumstances in their lives. Occupational therapists are not interested only in the person but see successful occupational performance arising as a function of a good match between a person's skills and abilities, the occupations they want and need to carry out and the environment within which these take place. Because of this, in addition to considering solutions that are focused on the person directly, they can also work with occupations and environments in a way that produces changes naturally in the person and therefore their occupational performance.

Becky was a 28 year old single parent and had been identified as having low intelligence, although not categorised as having learning difficulties. She had become depressed following the removal of her baby for adoption by social services, as it was considered to be at risk of harm through poor care and neglect. Previously Becky had lost her two older children for similar reasons. When she became pregnant with the third child she had hoped that she would be able to keep this one with support from social services. However, she had been unable to fulfil the parenting requirements expected of her.

Becky was seen in a day service since the GP and her support workers were concerned about her mental state and obvious self-neglect. Concerns had also been raised about her ability to look after her flat. She kept rats and had allowed them to mate and breed, which had caused additional problems.

The occupational therapist had been working through the Measure with Becky who had rated herself at 'mostly' on the statements so far, but had not really given any detail on why she had rated herself this way. She would simply say something like 'Well, I'm mostly able to do them.' As she was clearly fairly unkempt and unclean in her appearance at the interview, there was a concern arising in the therapist's mind when Becky had been answering questions 6 and 7 (Domestic and Personal Activities of Daily Living) in this way. A person may be considered to be at risk of self-neglect when this happens.

When the therapist asked question 13, 'I am able to achieve what I set out to do', Becky was silent for a while and then the following conversation took place:

BECKY: No, I don't think I can… I feel… umm… well, I've failed at most things I've tried… I couldn't even look after my little boy… he's been taken away… I do have some things… have some ideas of things I want to do… but I never seem to be able to… dunno… get to that point.

THERAPIST: So you have got some ideas of things you want to do but find it hard to get started because when you've tried hard to do things in the past it hasn't worked out for you?

BECKY: Yeah… that's right.

THERAPIST: That must be very hard to live with, thinking…

BECKY: …yeah, I think I'm useless, good for nothing really. I haven't really done anything I wanted to do, and… I don't like myself much.

Becky seemed to have given up on herself and her life. She had experienced so many losses and disappointments that she had given up wanting things and was apparently just going through the motions of living a life. When a client's situation is so problem-saturated it can be very helpful to ask a preferred future type of question, and when using the Measure, this can be done by focusing on what would be happening at 'definitely'. This allows the problems to be completely bypassed and because it is only a fantasy, the client can find it easier to give answers than if they thought it was limited by their apparently hopeless situation at present.

THERAPIST: OK, I'm going to ask you a difficult question, so you can take your time answering it. Let's imagine that you can answer 'definitely' to this one… that at some point I could ask you and you would say 'definitely'. You have a confidence in yourself that you can make things happen. Can you tell me a bit about what life would be like for you?

BECKY: I dunno…

THERAPIST: What would you be doing differently?

This question is a common question in solution focused brief therapy as it allows the session to focus on observable behavioural change. However, to an occupational therapist it provides a shift of focus away from the person and on to occupations.

BECKY: I might keep the flat a bit tidier… put a vase of flowers on the table… I quite like that look.

THERAPIST: Do you watch those house make-over programmes on TV?

BECKY: Yes… yes I do.

THERAPIST: When you are able to achieve what you set out to do, what would your flat look like?

The therapist is following Becky's lead and moves on to a discussion about environment.

BECKY: Well… mmm… I like that sort of purply colour, I think that's really nice… I think that would look nice in my room… I saw that the other day on one of those programmes. The room was really nice and it was set out nice, all in order… tidy, everything in a place. And I thought to myself, ooh I'd really like a room like that. I think there was a vase of flowers in that room… it just looked clean and I thought, that would be a really nice room to sit in. I'd like my room to be like that.

THERAPIST: OK, so when you are able to answer 'definitely', what else would be happening?

BECKY: You mean, like in a dream?

THERAPIST: Well yes, you could think of it in that way.

BECKY: Well, I've always… I've always… well, I don't think I could do it, but I've always wanted to work with animals. *(laughs)* But that would be a dream. But I'd have to look after myself before I can look after anyone else. But that would be my dream.

THERAPIST: What animals? What are your favourite animals?

BECKY: Well, all animals… but I like cats… and rats, I like them, I'm keeping them at home at the moment.

THERAPIST: So are you looking after them? I suppose you have to feed them, change their bedding?

BECKY: Well yes, but I'm not that good at it, not as good as I should be.

THERAPIST: What do you have to do to look after rats? Do you have to handle them?

BECKY: Yeah, they like to be touched and cuddled, they're very soppy. I really like getting them out of the cage and stroking them… and I have to feed them and give them water.

THERAPIST: So you are giving them what they need?

BECKY: Yeah… and I can tell which is male or female now and I keep them in separate cages. A couple of them got pregnant.

THERAPIST: So you had to learn to tell them apart?

BECKY: Yeah… it's important or they breed really quickly.

THERAPIST: Well, it sounds like you are looking after them and doing what needs to be done for them.

BECKY: Yes, I do love them.

THERAPIST: It sounds like you've tried a lot of things.

THERAPIST: So what would you be doing differently when you are at 'definitely'?

BECKY: Well, I would quite like to be doing it as a job.

THERAPIST: What difference would that make?

BECKY: Well, I could do it all the time… and I could show other people that I can care for something and look after something.

THERAPIST: So what else would other people see you doing?

BECKY: Well… I think they'd see me looking like I was taking care of myself. I'd have clean clothes. You know, sometimes I wear the same clothes day after day and some of them have cigarette burns. I might even have new clothes on. But I'm so big I don't know that I'd find any. I haven't bought any clothes for a long time, so I suppose that would be different.

THERAPIST: What sort of clothes would you be wearing?

BECKY: I don't know, I don't know what I could wear, I don't really like myself much. I would be too frightened to go shopping.

THERAPIST: OK, it sounds to me like you do still have some things you'd like to achieve, but it's also very hard to imagine doing them because your success in the past has been a bit hit and miss, is that right?

BECKY: Yeah, it doesn't seem worth it. I'm not good at anything, not good for anything.

THERAPIST: I'm curious – what are the things you want to achieve now?

BECKY: I'd like to get my flat in order… and… I'd like to start to eat better. I eat a lot of junk food and that's not good for me is it? I just go to the shop when

I'm hungry, I don't make proper meals… but I don't really know where to start with it…

THERAPIST: What else would you like to achieve?

BECKY: Well… I think I would like to do something about the way I look. Because I really… I don't like myself at all… and someone said to me that if I went to have my hair cut or did something to make myself look better I might feel better about myself. I know I'm still the same inside but, you know… if I went and, like, had my hair cut, it might make me like myself a little more.

THERAPIST: So… that's three things you said; the way you look after the house, what you're cooking and eating and the way you feel about yourself and your appearance.

BECKY: mmm hmm…

THERAPIST: So… which of those things would you feel like tackling first? You know the thing that would be the most useful or maybe would spur you on?

BECKY: err… it's hard to know where to start really.

THERAPIST: yeah…

BECKY: I think… I think… I think I need to get my flat sorted out first.

THERAPIST: So does that feel like quite a big…

BECKY: …yeah, the whole place is quite a tip really. I don't know where to start.

THERAPIST: What bothers you most at the moment, what would you like to change?

BECKY: I think it's my support workers. When they come they say, oh look Becky you haven't cleared up… and I know they think it smells.

THERAPIST: Do you think it smells?

BECKY: Well, I think I've just got used to it…

THERAPIST: Yeah, I think you do when you've got animals.

BECKY: Yeah the animals… and my smoking.

THERAPIST: So putting aside what they say about your flat, what would you like to change?

BECKY: Well, I think I'd like it to be tidier and cleaner... and, you know... I mean... there's... *(eyes brim with tears)*... I have a room upstairs and it's got all the baby stuff in... and I can't really even go in there. And I really need to do something about that room.

THERAPIST: Do you think that would be a tough room to tackle?

BECKY: Yes, I don't think I can face that yet but if I got one or two of the other rooms a bit tidier I could move on to that one.

THERAPIST: What needs to happen for you to tackle one room?

BECKY: I think I need some bin liners!

THERAPIST: Do you need to throw things away – are you a bit of a hoarder?

BECKY: A bit... but, it's more... you know when I sit and watch telly I eat and I just throw the wrappers on the floor and eat my sweets.

THERAPIST: Has it got to the stage where adding to it doesn't really make much difference?

BECKY: Yeah... and I like collecting videos and... music... and I think I've got too many. I'd like it to be like one of those smart rooms with a vase on the table.

THERAPIST: It could be a pretty big job, is there anyone who can help you?

BECKY: My foster mother would probably come and help me. But I haven't really thought of it... I haven't really thought about doing anything... not till just now. She could come round and help me choose the colour of the walls.

THERAPIST: It's good to have someone to help... it can seem so big until you start...

BECKY: I suppose if I could clear a few things out, then it would be a bit clearer and maybe she could come and help me paint the walls.

THERAPIST: Are you saying you'd like to get rid of a few bags before she came?

BECKY: I could… I could try…

THERAPIST: Maybe just to fill two bin bags?

BECKY: Yeah I could try. I think it's rubbish day on Friday so if I could try to get it done by then…

THERAPIST: Would it be easier to do it in little stages like that?

BECKY: Yeah. If I started with the living room, I think that would be a good place to start… and then… I suppose I could ask her round, ask her if she could help me choose a colour for the walls.

THERAPIST: It sounded like you had some idea for that already, this purply colour.

BECKY: Yeah, that's what I'd like.

THERAPIST: So, here we are, we've got something that you definitely can achieve, you have an idea of what you'd like to have, you've got an idea of who can help you… what else do you think you'd be doing to help keep you on-track, keep you focused, so you can get what you set out to achieve?

BECKY: What with my living room?

THERAPIST: Yes, I'm just curious what else, when you are definitely able to achieve what you set out to do… what else will you be doing to keep focused on your goal?

BECKY: …Do you think you might be able to help me with that?

THERAPIST: Well yes, that's definitely possible. I mean… well, I do have some ideas but only if you think it would be helpful…

BECKY: That's the kind of help I need. Someone to say 'have you done that?', help me work out what's the next step.

THERAPIST: And what about your support workers? Can they

provide some of the help you need?

BECKY: Well, I've been seeing them for a while. They generally do the same things each time, help with everyday stuff. I hadn't really thought about the… the questions you've asked me… I hadn't really thought about having something as exciting as having that happen. They've just been trying to get me to do everyday things. There didn't seem much point before.

THERAPIST: Do you think there might be some point to that now?

BECKY: Yeah, probably.

Outcome

Becky responded really well to breaking tasks down into small stages or steps. The occupational therapist worked very closely with her, giving lots of encouragement and support and helping her plan achievable steps. They both met together with the support workers to plan some of the tasks that Becky wanted help with.

Over a number of weeks, Becky gradually began to make changes. She felt spurred on to do more when she started achieving her goals. Once she had spring-cleaned her living room, she asked her foster mother to help her paint it. She was so pleased with the finished result that she wanted to keep it tidy and clean.

Becky and the occupational therapist went out together to buy her some new clothes, which helped her feel much better about herself and more able to face the more difficult challenges like clearing the baby's room.

'Reputation to Recover'

The first time someone is admitted to an acute in-patient unit can be a terrifying time. It often happens as a result of a period of distress and confusion which adds to the fear of finding oneself in an unfamiliar situation. John, 23, was admitted to hospital following a psychotic episode associated with increasing cannabis abuse. He had isolated himself in his room, stopped going to work and was neglecting himself and his flat. John's flatmate, Keith, was concerned about him and tried to get him to sort himself out, but John mistook Keith's concern and ended up hitting him.

Once in hospital John quickly calmed down and after three weeks with no cannabis, had regained his composure. In such situations, it is important to help people regain their lifestyle as soon as possible to avoid institutionalisation. Occupational therapists can be key to community re-integration.

In the following conversation it can be seen that the therapist's main aim was to draw out and emphasise John's strengths and resources. John felt he had lost everything through his behaviour and was in danger of becoming demoralised, hopeless and depressed. This interview is an example of how a solution focused conversation can restore hope.

Let us start at question 2:

'I have satisfying relationships'

JOHN: What does that mean?

THERAPIST: Well, it's to do with how you think you interact with people, your family or friends – whether you feel good about the way it's gone, if you think you relate well – that sort of thing.

JOHN: Mostly. If it feels safe, alright but otherwise I don't enjoy being with people.

THERAPIST: Is that something you would like to change?

JOHN: Yes… because I feel lonely.

THERAPIST: So what would be different if you were moving from mostly up to definitely?

JOHN: I don't know. Mostly I just talk to Keith in the flat with me – he gets fed up with me.

THERAPIST: OK, so if you were at definitely and your relationships were more satisfying, what would Keith notice different about you?

JOHN: He'd be less bothered by me…

THERAPIST: Do you think he's bothered by you?

JOHN: Yeah... I'm worried he might not want to know me any more... but he does... he hasn't, like said he doesn't want to know me... but I think he finds me irritating.

THERAPIST: So if you weren't irritating – I don't know if you are irritating, I know it's natural to worry about the way we come across, but let's say that Keith was comfortable with you, what would be different?

JOHN: I'd have more people to go out with and talk to.

THERAPIST: So what difference would that make?

JOHN: I wouldn't be so bored, that would be better.

'I have confidence in myself'

JOHN: *(long pause)*... I have times where I do feel I can do things well.

THERAPIST: What's happening at those times?

JOHN: At work I was building a wall... I got really absorbed in it... it was just right... you know, working really well. It felt great... at the end I'd done something really good, I felt proud, good about myself.

John was describing clearly a high level of occupational engagement, possibly even 'flow'. He was already beginning to provide an answer to question 16, 'I can get so involved in a project or activity that I can forget about my discomfort/problems.' This is not a problem. The occupational therapist saw this response as an opportunity to explore John's skills.

THERAPIST: ...building a wall... that takes a lot of skill, I know because I've done it badly, having thought it couldn't be that difficult. *(laughs)* So tell me, how do you do it? How do you get a wall straight?

JOHN: Well, if you haven't done it very many times, you use your level, use it slowly while you build it and it stays level. The trick is... the trick is to do it reasonably quickly so you've got your mortar so it will float the bricks *(John is now sitting forward, using his hands to demonstrate)...* the more you mess around with it, you will lose the float, so you need to do it at the right speed.

THERAPIST: But that's amazing – how do you know when to not fiddle with it?

JOHN: You can put your level on it and check but you should be able to do it just with your eye.

THERAPIST: Wow.

JOHN: Looking at it and seeing, *(John is now fully immersed in imagining himself building the wall)* measure, gently adjust, level it, then the next one, and the next one. But the more you do it, the more you can feel it and more...

THERAPIST: So you sort of become attuned to it?

JOHN: Yes, that's exactly right. And the more you're doing that the less you think and you just do the next brick, the next brick... It's very satisfying.

This interchange allowed a shift in the balance of expertise. John was now clearly the expert and he was experiencing a sense of confidence in himself. The therapist found an important aspect of John's life and a definite work skill that John values.

THERAPIST: Yes, I bet it is... are there any other things you do where you get that feeling?

JOHN: No not really.

THERAPIST: What about close to getting it?

JOHN: Well, I listen to music and that works.

'I can stand up for myself'

JOHN: I can fight.

THERAPIST: OK... I guess what this question is about, what I'm interested in is if you can stand up for yourself without having to fight but also not be, like, a doormat.

JOHN: It's difficult... Yeah... I dunno... I tend to overreact. I think if someone's having a go at me,

I'll square up to them.

THERAPIST: It must be quite hard. I mean I don't find myself in those sorts of situations so I don't know what it's like to be kind of threatened in that way.

Once more the therapist made John the expert, without making judgements about his fighting but by simply being curious.

JOHN: Well, it's just... once well... it's like building the wall actually... if you react at the right time, you're shouting louder, more physical than the other person, then they back down... but... I don't know... see, sometimes all these things just happen and you get to a point where you're so angry about what's just happened and you feel insulted, you've lost your face and you feel small, made small by somebody else. I dunno, it's like for me, everything's either alright or it's a battle. I can't find the words to just not go there.

THERAPIST: It does sound to me like being able to fight and stand up for yourself in those kind of situations is something that's helped you survive.

JOHN: Yeah, but the other side of it is you feel scared and your heart's pounding and you kind of feel sick and it's... and it's all too much. You know you can't talk to someone and you wanna cry, but you can't. It's horrible, it's horrible.

The therapist listened carefully to what John was saying. Instead of focusing on the problem that John was describing and getting caught up in the emotional content, she has been practicing 'constructive listening'. In other words she was looking for evidence of strengths and qualities in everything John said. At this point she chose to feed back an observation. This had the effect of reframing John's behaviour into something more understandable and acceptable and thus easier to build on.

THERAPIST: *(long pause)* I'm curious really, about something you just said about... it sounds to me that it's quite important to you... well, you said you didn't like

>   to be made to feel small, so it sounds to me like
>   your dignity is really important to you.
>
> JOHN: Yeah.
>
> THERAPIST: To feel that you're recognised as a person…
>
> JOHN: Yes, I feel people are laughing at me. That they feel
>   they're better than me, that they're more important
>   than I am. I know that's what they're thinking and
>   I don't like it, I don't want them to. I want them to
>   treat me properly.
>
> THERAPIST: Yeah. So if people were treating you with dignity,
>   what difference would that make to you, what
>   would you be doing?
>
> JOHN: I wouldn't be fighting.
>
> THERAPIST: What would you be doing instead of fighting?
>
> JOHN: *(stunned silence)* I suppose I'd just be friendly.

This conversation provided some important information about John. From a problem-focused point of view, one might describe him as having poor anger-management and begin to formulate ideas for interventions. However, from a solution focused point of view, of more interest is the fact that John is clearly someone who wants to have pride in himself, who wants to be respected and treated with dignity. From an occupational therapy point of view one would also not necessarily focus on anger-management but consider that if he were to change his environment so he did not get into violent situations, or if he were to gain confidence and respect in other areas of his life, his ability to manage his anger would naturally arise or develop.

'I can make decisions when I need to'

The following interchange illustrates how the hospital environment affects a person's sense of efficacy. John had lost touch with familiar everyday situations which contributed to his sense of loss and fear about having ruined his life. The occupational therapist can help by normalising the experience and offering some tangible options:

> THERAPIST: OK, 'I can make decisions when I need to.'
>
> JOHN: I have done… at the moment it's hard because

there's no 'yes or no', no clarity. Whatever I do is going to turn to crap. I can't understand the decisions that are there.

THERAPIST: What sort of decisions do you feel you're faced with at the moment then?

JOHN: Well, it's about doing the right thing... you know... In the flat and with mates... and how I deal with what's happening at the moment.

THERAPIST: So when you make decisions and you feel you have done the right thing, how do you do that?

JOHN: I don't know... it's my... it's what I want to do... it's what's right for the situation. I don't know... maybe that's why decisions are so hard to make... maybe I can't know, maybe I won't know until...

THERAPIST: So if you were moving up towards 'definitely' what would be the first signs that you were beginning to get back that ability? Any small signs.

JOHN: Umm...

THERAPIST: Because here in hospital a lot of things are decided for you aren't they?

JOHN: Yeah.

THERAPIST: So thinking about here in hospital are there any things that would give you a sense that you're beginning to make decisions for yourself?

JOHN: To go out.

THERAPIST: OK. When have you been out?

JOHN: Not for the last two weeks.

THERAPIST: Yes. Are you happy to go on?

JOHN: Yes, it's good actually.

THERAPIST: OK, the next questions are all things that us occupational therapists are very curious about. ' I can take care of my home environment.'

JOHN: I like the set-up. I live with Keith in our flat-share and that's good but I think that Keith's a bit fed up with me. There's things around the flat that I haven't been doing, I used to do them, but in the last couple of months everything has just slid a bit.

THERAPIST: Is that housework type of things?

JOHN: Yeah and about coming back and you know just little things. I think it's great, my room is great, I feel great when I'm in my room, it's a great space.

THERAPIST: How long have you and Keith been sharing a flat?

JOHN: Couple of years now.

THERAPIST: What's your room like then?

JOHN: It's just little, got a bed in it, my stereo, not much to look at, window looks out over the road. But it's nice.

THERAPIST: So what are you like then in the flat – are you stereotypical blokes, messy with remnants of curry around or…

JOHN: *(laughs)* Well yes, well, that's probably more true for me. Keith's a bit more house-proud and I guess that's part of the problem. I can't always do things the way he would like them to be. He keeps things nice and tidy. You know I'm just a mess.

THERAPIST: Are you always a mess or is that more recently?

JOHN: Well, it's got much worse in the last couple of months before I came here. It was pretty bad, I just couldn't be bothered. I stayed in my room most of the time, I didn't come out at all. It just got worse. I was going to get round to doing things but it just didn't happen you know. And Keith got pretty pissed off with me.

THERAPIST: Was it just being pissed off? Was he just pissed off?

JOHN: Well, I guess he was also worried about me it was… It was… it kind of felt he was having a go at me at the time.

THERAPIST: What – he was trying to get you to do stuff?

JOHN: Yeah, I'd not been to work. He was saying, come on, get up, get washed do a bit around the house.

THERAPIST: Did it feel like he was nagging?

JOHN: Yes, at the time I couldn't do it, it was too much, I couldn't do it.

THERAPIST: In general though you want to go back there? *(John nods)* So what was happening when things were going well?

JOHN: Well, Keith goes to work and he gives me a lift to work. And we'd go out a couple of evenings a week, to the pub or cinema.

THERAPIST: Keith was satisfied with your level of housework at that point?

JOHN: Well yes, we'd take turns to cook and wash up we had a rota and it was pretty good but then I sort of stopped doing that, you know I'd just eat take-aways. I couldn't be bothered. In fact I stopped eating for a while.

THERAPIST: Well that would worry me if I was your flatmate.

JOHN: Yeah I suppose now it seems silly, but at the time it seemed like the right thing to do.

THERAPIST: You know I've heard this sort of thing before, and I know it does happen and I don't think it's silly. But I suppose I kind of think about being Keith and how I might feel if my flatmate, my friend, was behaving like that.

JOHN: I didn't really think about Keith… well, I did, but it was kind of in a different way.

In this last part of the conversation the therapist situated John's behaviour within normalising frames of reference. Firstly, in terms of letting John know that he is not the only person who has found themselves in this distressing situation and secondly giving him the opportunity to view Keith's behaviour from a difference perspective.

'I can take care of myself'

THERAPIST: Washing etc. Whatever 'taking care of yourself' means.

JOHN: If I take care of myself I like the idea of, on a Friday night being able to dress up really well. Go out and 'do the town'.

THERAPIST: What does that mean then?

JOHN: Just go out, go to pubs, you know.

THERAPIST: Do you feel good dressed up?

JOHN: Yeah 'cos during the day, on the site when you're pretty dirty, greasy and then you go out and look like something pretty flash.

THERAPIST: So what's your best dressed up outfit then?

JOHN: Well, I've my Armani suit

THERAPIST: You've got an Armani suit?! Wow!

JOHN: Yes, it looks… it holds me upright, makes me look good. *(John sits upright)*

THERAPIST: So you scrub up well?

JOHN: *(laughs)* Yes, suited and booted.

THERAPIST: What about on an everyday basis taking care of yourself. You do quite a physical job…

JOHN: Well, I don't do any exercise, you know workout… but I don't need to.

THERAPIST: What's it like here, what's it like on the ward?

JOHN: Actually it's not so bad. I didn't like it at first. You know gotta get things done at certain times. But the last week was OK, doing things, got into my own clothes, washing… yeah it feels a bit better because I wasn't bothering at all before.

THERAPIST: So is the routine helping you?

JOHN: Yes I guess so. I'm surprised because I don't like that kind of thing, someone else telling me what to do, but the last couple of weeks it's felt quite good. I know what I've got to do, get dressed, be up and washed you know and then do some work with the nurses, so I know what I'm supposed to be doing so… which is alright.

'I am able to take care of the place where I live'

THERAPIST: We have already talked about that a bit. Do we need to talk about – anything to add?

JOHN: I quite like ironing.

THERAPIST: Do you?

JOHN: Yes, when you go out on Friday and you iron your shirt it's really satisfying, you put it on, you look good... but also in the last few months that's really dwindled.

THERAPIST: It does sound to me you're a man who likes a job well done.

JOHN: Well yes that's probably fair I do. But it's all or nothing, if I can't do it well I do nothing. But that's probably true, yeah.

'I can manage my finances'

JOHN: Well, I earned good money when I was on the site and a lot of it was cash in hand. I've never been short of cash. If I wanted something I could put the money away for that, like my Armani suit.

THERAPIST: So you actually saved for that?

JOHN: Yes, if I want something I'll decide that and put money away for it.

THERAPIST: Where did you learn to do that?

JOHN: I don't know, I've always done it. I guess my Mum did it, if she needed new shoes for us, she'd do it. It's not difficult, it's alright, if you're working you can do it.

Within the last few questions, the therapist managed to elicit a number of positive traits that John has been able to identify from when his life was going better. Reminiscing and remembering these more positive times may help John to envisage his life like that again.

THERAPIST: But generally I do get the impression that with Keith you were beginning to get into arrears?

JOHN: Ah yes, well yes. I'd been smoking a bit of blow, of

dope, around the time when things started falling apart. I borrowed a bit of money from Keith. Actually it's quite a lot of money now and it got a bit out of hand. I owe him a couple of hundred quid and I didn't pay the rent for two months. So I owe him a lot of money so that's another thing that's making things difficult to go back.

THERAPIST: It sounds to me like generally speaking you can do these things, but in the last couple of months, for whatever reason things have fallen apart a bit and you've ended up doing things you wouldn't naturally be doing...

JOHN: Well, it feels like I've ended up in a bit of a pit and everything's gone haywire and it just gets worse and worse.

THERAPIST: It sounds quite overwhelming.

The therapist therefore maintained a focus on John as a person rather than getting too interested in his problems and problem behaviour. This helps to re-establish a person's identity and confidence. It is this type of focus which supports client-centred rather than condition or problem-centred practice. As the conversation continues you will see that the therapist continues to build on the rapport she is forming with John by gently introducing possibilities for moving forward. Solution focused 'purists' might feel this is too directive and that the client should come up with all their solutions. However, when a person has lost their roles and sense of identity, is as overwhelmed by events and loss of self-control as John, and in an unfamiliar and uncertain environment like an acute in-patient mental health unit, it is hard to know where the first step might be. The suggestions the therapist makes in the following conversation are directly related to what John's occupational interests might be and act as beacons of hope.

JOHN: Yeah, it is and I can't... you know I'm embarrassed about what's happened and... you know with Keith, and I feel I've messed him about and given him a hard time and I have... and I've got to try...

I don't know what to do.

THERAPIST: Well, again that's something we can work together on finding a way through for you. You've obviously got a lot of skills and abilities and so the path through is made easier because there are lots of things we know you can do. 'Organising your week' – planning your week in a way that works for you.

JOHN: Well, you know we were talking about the weeks that were good. Things went... well, we were sorted. Then everything fell apart and it was like just too difficult to go back.

THERAPIST: So when you were able to organise yourself what did you structure your week around?

JOHN: Well, I always had to turn up to work! Friday nights... they were the main things you know, I'd work for the Friday night.

THERAPIST: What about household things? You mentioned something about rotas.

JOHN: Yes, we didn't have things written down but we kind of agreed that I'd do it on Mondays and Wednesdays. The rest of the stuff... Keith's always been better at doing things than me, like cleaning the bathroom and stuff.

THERAPIST: So was there a time when Keith sort of pushing you to do things was good for you?

JOHN: Yeah it was. It made me do things I wouldn't have done otherwise, and actually looking back now it was quite good 'cos when I lost that everything fell apart.

THERAPIST: You mentioned you were surprised to find that here on the ward even though you didn't like being told what to do, the nurses encouraging you to do things turned out to be quite helpful.

JOHN: Yeah, I don't like the idea of it at all, but...

THERAPIST: I think it's something to think about. I know I find it really hard to structure my time when I haven't got something specific to do.

JOHN: Yeah, no, I wasn't very good at that either.

'I'm able to calm myself when needed'

THERAPIST: That's sort of about when you're feeling anxious or afraid or scared, those sorts of feelings.

JOHN: Well, I don't really. I'm not very good at that. I've err… I got into having a bit of blow and a bit of a drink to… you know, that was just to really – that was just to sort of… when I was getting upset, or kind of a bit anxious and… it worked actually.

THERAPIST: Did it continue working?

JOHN: Well sort of… it just made more things difficult to do, that was the thing. It did keep me calmer. Also I got a bit paranoid on the whacky backy but it still made me feel a bit calmer than without.

THERAPIST: Have you tried any other ways of calming yourself down apart from…? I ask because what you're doing is sort of giving yourself medicine, you're self-medicating.

JOHN: Yes exactly – it's like the private sector isn't it?

THERAPIST: *(laughs)* Yes I suppose so. That's a good way of putting it. I mean some people might go to the doctor's and ask for tranquillisers or something.

JOHN: Yes, I don't like going to doctors.

THERAPIST: Yeah but you're still sort of taking medicines to solve that problem. I was just wondering if there were any other ways that you've come across that have worked without any substances going into your body.

JOHN: Well, actually when I have a smoke or a drink I listen to music and it helps.

THERAPIST: Any particular type of music?

JOHN: Yes well, last time I was sort of too stoned to work it out but it was Radio 3 and I was really into it, I didn't know what it was though but I was really into it.

THERAPIST: OK, so that's sort of classical music?

JOHN: I don't know – I mean lots of music does it but that was nice and slow very gentle.

THERAPIST: OK, actually we have a lot of CDs down in the OT department and there might be a music group going on next week.

JOHN: Oh I'd be really up for that, yes, but I don't know the names of anything.

THERAPIST: Well, you could maybe find out.

THERAPIST: So when you think of times when you are relaxed and chilled out, what's happening at those times?

JOHN: I like to... err... just think about good things, you know good times?

THERAPIST: Are there any particular times you think about?

JOHN: Well, me and Keith had a holiday in Ibiza and... it was nice being on the beach with the water, it was just nice, nice atmosphere in the sun. I think of things like that.

THERAPIST: OK, well that might be an area where we could explore some alternatives, we could have a look at. That's the sort of thing I could do as an occupational therapist.

JOHN: Yeah that sounds good.

'I have positive ways of coping with angry feelings'

JOHN: (groans, puts head in hands) Well, I don't really. When I get into a rage you know it's just gets more and more and I end up with such a headache at the end of... and you know, so upset and frightened, you know I broke the door on my cabinet in my bedroom. And you know that wasn't very good.

I broke where I kept my CDs, lots of my CDs got broken. That was stupid.

THERAPIST: So when you are more in control of your anger, what's different about those times – I mean you can't have reacted like that all the time or you wouldn't have done all the things you've done.

JOHN: Well, I've done it a lot. And it's you know... The difficult thing is you know, when do you start? I mean 'cos it's all or nothing and when you front up someone and you're sort of straight into it. Straight into like feeling frightened and all that.

THERAPIST: So are your angry feelings all to do with a confrontation with another person or do you have angry feelings at other times?

JOHN: Well I... the last few months I've been feeling angry all the time you know. I got angry with Keith and I hit him and you know, he reckoned it was about nothing but I thought it was all about... you know... well that he was about to hit me but he said it wasn't, nothing like that at all, he was just asking me a question about something and I thought I had to hit him...

THERAPIST: It sounds like a really confusing time.

JOHN: Yeah it's all been very, very strange.

THERAPIST: I can't imagine you liking being like that just from what you've told me about yourself.

JOHN: No, I don't... No, I felt very frightened, I felt everybody was like wanting to have a go at me. Like everyone was attacking me. I felt like I was being more and more pushed into a place where I couldn't get out and the only way out was to hit back. You know that's what I mean... you were asking about decisions, and that was trying to make a decision. I made the wrong decision.

THERAPIST: Getting back to control over your feelings and what we can do here…

JOHN: Yeah I've got to do something about it… I can't live like that… I can't live like that. I won't be able to live there, I won't have any friends, I've got to do something…

'I'm able to achieve what I set out to do'

THERAPIST: So when you set out to do something can you make it happen?

JOHN: *(laughs)* Yeah, yeah – it's making that decision to do it. I mean you know I got my suit. And when I got my City and Guilds, you know I went to college to do it. And I got it and that pissed off a lot of people because they didn't think I'd do it.

THERAPIST: *(laughs)* OK, tell me a bit more about that.

JOHN: It's just people thought that I wouldn't be able to do it and that sort of stuff. I knew I could.

THERAPIST: So you proved them wrong?

JOHN: Yeah.

THERAPIST: So how did you know that you could do it?

JOHN: Well, I just looked at some of the other people who got it on the site and I thought well I can work as well as they can. I can do as well as them. What they did – well they were all lording it up a bit – but I thought what they're doing is no different to what I'm doing but I knew they wouldn't believe that I could do it.

THERAPIST: So how did people react?

JOHN: Oh it was sweet. I just sort of dropped it into the conversation, 'I've got my City and Guilds now', and they were surprised and I got a bit of respect.

THERAPIST: So did you have to work incredibly hard to do it.

JOHN: Yeah I was alright at the practical stuff I'm good at that but I'm not that good at the written stuff but Keith gave me a lot of help with that.

THERAPIST: Did you get better at it?

JOHN: Yeah I did – well I passed it. I'm not sure I'd be able to do the same thing now.

THERAPIST: Are there any other times when you've done what other people haven't expected?

JOHN: Hmm – that was the best.

'I'm able to maintain attention and concentration on things that are important'

JOHN: Yeah if they're important to me. (pause) But the last few months it's been impossible, the more I smoke the harder I find it to do anything.

THERAPIST: So the smoking interfered with your concentration?

JOHN: Yeah yeah, it did.

'I'm able to solve problems as they arise'

JOHN: Oh, no, not really. No.

THERAPIST: 'Sometimes' or 'not at all'?

JOHN: Well I have done... No it's 'sometimes' it's not 'not at all'.

THERAPIST: So what problems have you solved?

JOHN: Well, since being in here I've worked out how things are organised. I know how to deal with the way things are set up. I know that if I get up, get dressed, get organised...

THERAPIST: What about things in the flat, like if a fuse goes?

JOHN: I can do that, if stuff breaks I can fix it. It's sort of things like if we get a demand for the phone bill or something. Bills and things like that. Keith is much more on top of it. I mean my reaction to problems was thumping Keith. But I know that's a problem. I've been trying to think it through, think of different ways of dealing with it, but it's hard.

THERAPIST: Yes it is. I completely agree with you. It is hard, especially when you've been used to doing things in one way for a long time. Change is hard, but it's not impossible.

'I can enjoy myself'

JOHN: Well, at the moment it feels like it would be bad to enjoy myself. I mean after what I've done, what I've done to other people it would be wrong.

THERAPIST: So do you feel a bit that you have to punish yourself?

JOHN: Yeah I mean I've behaved so badly to all these people… I shouldn't really enjoy myself. I mean I've made all these people's lives so miserable over the past few months… it's not right. But I used to… I mean like on a Friday night, we used to have a right laugh.

THERAPIST: *(long pause)* I'm just reflecting on what you've just said. What I'm hearing all the time is someone who cares about what people think of them. Someone who cares and want to make a good impression.

JOHN: Yeah I suppose you're right – you're judged by other people and at the end of the day you want to get on with people, you want friends, people who can respect you.

THERAPIST: So you kind of feel that you need to get your reputation back?

JOHN: Yeah well, I feel like I should move and I should move away to where nobody knows me. 'Cos all the people who know me are just going to say 'that nutter'. I mean it's always going to be at the back of people's minds.

THERAPIST: Yes, maybe, but then again they've also known you in different circumstances when you've been a person who's put in a day's work…

JOHN: Yeah but people judge you on the worst things don't they?

THERAPIST: Is that the way you judge people?

JOHN: Yeah of course. That's what people do – 'there's that bloke over there, he's done that bad thing', they're not going to say 'there's that bloke over there he's done a bad thing but he's done lots of good things too.'

THERAPIST: Well maybe. I don't know.

'I take enough exercise'

JOHN: Yeah, I do a physical job.

THERAPIST: But what about recently - you've haven't been at work for a while? How are your fitness levels?

JOHN: Yeah that's true, I hadn't thought of that. I haven't been at work for four months or so, just been lying around in the flat, smoking dope and drinking. One of the nurses took me out for a walk, first time I'd been outside for ages. And I really felt it, it felt good actually.

'I get enough rest and sleep'

JOHN: When I was at work, it was good. I'd work hard all day. It's really physical and I'd get tired out and it was good eventually to get to bed. But in the last few months it's just been… those weeks were… I don't know if I even slept. I think I was awake for days and days, just thinking about things. I don't think I divided things up into nights and days, things like that.

THERAPIST: What about since you've been on the ward?

JOHN: Yeah it's better. That's another thing, there's time for bed and time to get up. And I've got some medication as well they've given me, it has helped. The sleep was something that was really… you know… I mean, not being able to get to sleep and waking up and worrying and thinking… it was miserable.

THERAPIST: It sounds like you were in quite a vicious circle.

JOHN: Yeah.

THERAPIST: Like things were going wrong and everything kind of...

JOHN: Yeah. It does feel like things are changing a bit now.

'I have people who support and understand me'

JOHN: Well I did, do, I mean Keith was a big friend and a big help but since I...

THERAPIST: Have you seen Keith since you were in hospital?

JOHN: Yeah he's been in. He's got a new girlfriend... that's a bit weird 'cos... well she sees me as a bit of a nutter. But you know he's turned up to see me even though I clocked him and he hasn't said anything like you can't come home or anything like that. He's been OK about it all. But you can see he's worried about me coming home. But he's seen me through when I was at my worst.

THERAPIST: Anyone else apart from Keith?

JOHN: No.

THERAPIST: What about in the past?

JOHN: No.

THERAPIST: So you've been coping on your own for a long time?

JOHN: Yeah, well when I lived at home my Mum looked after me, did my washing and so on but we didn't really talk. I mean with Keith we could talk.

THERAPIST: Is that something you'd like to change?

JOHN: Well yeah, I guess now that Keith's met this person and I guess they'll want to move in together. And I won't have anyone and it's really nice having someone to talk to. He'd give you good answers and help give you a different idea of how to respond to a situation.

'I can make positive goals'

JOHN: I think I can now. I mean nothing too wild, just doing anything to get back home, start to repair what's happened. I want to pay Keith back what I owe him. I mean that would go some way to repairing what's happened, to apologise. Set it right, well, things will never be right I mean what's happened's happened but it would go some way.

This is the last question on the Measure. At this point the therapist paused, collected her thoughts, set out the whole Measure in front of her and John so they could look over the whole form together and gave some positive feedback about the conversation before moving on, ask John about the changes he wanted to make and the small steps he could take.

THERAPIST: We've talked about an awful lot of different things and I've picked up some things about you which I've noticed and I've mentioned some of them already, which are that I think you've obviously got a lot of useful skills and for a lot of your life you've managed alright for yourself. The thing that's really impressed me is this sense that you like to feel that you are a good person, that you like to feel proud of yourself and that you enjoy it when you feel you are living up to your own expectations. Is that fair?

JOHN: Yeah I think that's right. It is now, it wasn't a few weeks ago.

THERAPIST: It seems to me that's what you're basically like. And yes, you've had a confusing time and it sounds like things got rather out of hand, and you know… that happens to people. I could have opinions about that and I suppose that people have suggested reasons why that might have happened, maybe have told you some of those things, but I'm not going to, I'm just going to say that I think there are a lot of things we can work with and that give me the sense that you should be able to work your way out of this pit you've put yourself in. And moving towards some of the things that you'd like to have change. So what I'm really interested in from that point of view... What are the main areas you want to see change happen?

JOHN: Well, I don't want it to happen again, I don't want to get into the situation where I mess up.

THERAPIST: So what do you have to develop?

JOHN: Well, I think at the moment I have to talk to people, so if I'm going down the same route I can see another way of dealing with it. Well, we were talking about Keith and the flat and that and I want to work towards getting back to that, when things were working and I want to pay Keith back his money so I need to get back to work.

THERAPIST: There's stuff that we can offer you, ways to work together that we can discuss in a minute, but I'm interested in whether there are some small steps that you think you can take now, maybe in the next few days? Any small things that you could do?

JOHN: Well, it would be good to talk to Keith again, to reassure him, you know... What's been going on so far on the ward, you know getting shaved, dressed, more of a routine, that's been good. But I'd like to get some more clothes. I've been wearing the same things. I'd like to contact my old job.

THERAPIST: Do they know you've been in hospital?

JOHN: No.

THERAPIST: So they think...

JOHN: Think that I just walked off the site, yes. But the bloke who was in charge, actually he was a pretty good bloke and I think he'd understand, you know they might, they might consider taking me back on.

THERAPIST: Well, it did sound like when you were working you were an asset.

JOHN: Oh yes, before I left I was there every day, I worked hard.

THERAPIST: So are you going to give Keith a ring?

JOHN: Yes, I'll do that.

Outcome

John stayed in hospital for another three weeks. From the information John provided in the interview he and the occupational therapist worked out a programme he could follow. John was keen to improve his fitness so although he was not interested in gardening as a hobby, he decided to join the gardening group so he could dig and spend time outdoors. In the third week before he left, he spent two whole days in the garden digging over vegetable beds. He joined the music group and found some classical CDs that he liked. The therapist worked with John to develop a relaxation tape based on his memories of Ibiza and other relaxing images. The occupational therapist suggested that John could use the occupational therapy kitchen to cook a lunch and invite Keith and his girlfriend. This proved a real success and went a long way to helping John feel that he could demonstrate his recovery to his friend. Going on a home visit was also very important to him and motivated him to focus on positive goals for the future. The occupational therapist also helped him to re-establish links with his former employer and John was eventually able to return to work. He was keen to attend an anger management group in the community and the occupational therapist referred him to one running in the day service. John was motivated to stop smoking cannabis and use other ways to calm himself. He also became interested in how routines supported his occupations and used worksheet Q10 to develop a weekly routine.

Writing Strength–Based Reports

Shifting our focus in practice from problem-focused to solution-focused meant that we began to consider how it affected other areas of our practice. It quickly became clear that there was little point in carrying out a solution-focused interview and then using the information to formulate a problem or deficit-based report. It could be tempting to look at the answers to the Measure and report only on the areas where the client has answered 'not at all' or 'sometimes', and see this as an indication of areas where change would be desirable. However, these areas may not be significant to the client or a priority for change. It is important to remember that the Measure does not provide an empirical assessment of the client, but is an interview tool, so the therapist is drawing on their reasoning and observation skills to understand the client's wants and needs from the collaborative dialogue that has taken place. Working from a solution-focused perspective, identifying strengths and resources and focusing and highlighting these in the conversation are all considered powerful interventions which improve the chances of a positive outcome for the client. Occupational therapy also has the tradition of focusing on ability, rather than disability or deficit, as the building block for positive change and increasing motivation. This has sometimes been subsumed through working within a medical model of healthcare delivery. Working in a solution-focused way helps to restore confidence in this traditional perspective.

Here is an example of a strengths-based report about John, the client presented above.

Name: John

Background

John was admitted to the ward following a violent incident involving his flatmate, Keith. John's mental health had apparently deteriorated over a period of two months, possibly as a result of increasing cannabis use. John had stopped going to work and had isolated himself in his room. He had stopped doing his personal and domestic activities of daily living and his sleep patterns had become severely disturbed.

Progress since admission

John has responded well to the routine of the ward and reports benefits from the medication he has been prescribed.

Strengths identified

John has a well-developed work history as a builder. He is a skilled bricklayer and has undertaken qualifications to support his career. Prior to his mental deterioration he was a valued worker. His self-care skills are appropriate to his age and situation, both in terms of his personal and domestic activities of daily living. He was able to share a flat for three years successfully. He is able to budget and save money. He enjoys age and gender-appropriate activities with his flatmate; getting dressed up and going out at the weekend, playing pool and drinking. John's main strength is his sense of pride and his identity as a person who is decent, honest and dependable.

Resources identified

John has a strong friendship with Keith, his flatmate, who appears to still want John to return to the flat despite the events during his unstable period. John also reports that he may be able to regain his job due his previous good record and an understanding boss. He has shown ability to study and gain qualifications and to use support when necessary.

Priorities for change

John's confidence has been shaken by events prior to admission and his main priority is to ensure it does not happen again. He has some insight into the role abuse of cannabis may have played in his problems and is interested in exploring some alternative relaxation strategies. He has identified his volatile anger as a source of stress in himself and his relationships with others and would like to develop his anger management strategies. John is eager to return home but acknowledges that he must address his relationship with Keith and in particular, the money he owes him. John's social life is very much dependent on Keith at present and as Keith now has a girlfriend John has realised that he probably needs to develop a wider social network.

Agreed strategy for change

OT and John will plan a home visit as soon as possible so

John can prepare for leaving hospital and returning home and also collect some clothing.

John will attend the gardening group in order to regain physical strength and fitness for work.

John will use the kitchen to regain his confidence in cooking and also invite Keith to eat a meal he has prepared so he can demonstrate his improvement.

John will attend the music group to determine which music might be useful for relaxation.

OT and John will work together to develop a relaxation tape.

John will notice how routine supports his occupations and use Worksheet Q10 to develop a satisfying weekly routine.

John will contact his previous employer to explain his absence and explore possibilities for return to work.

OT will refer John to a community-based anger management group.

Signatures:

John   Occupational Therapist
Date: 01/01/01

References and Recommended Reading

Burgess, K (2004) personal communications

Cade, B and O'Hanlon, WH (1993) *A Brief Guide to Brief Therapy* New York: W.W. Norton & Company

Canadian Association of Occupational Therapists (CAOT) (2004) *Enabling Occupation*

Hasselkus, BR (2002) *The Meaning of Everyday Occupation.* Thorofare, NJ: Slack Inc.

De Shazer, S (1985) *Keys to Solution in Brief Therapy.* New York: W.W. Norton & Company

De Shazer, S (1994) *Words Were Originally Magic* New York: W.W. Norton & Company

Department of Health (DOH) (1999) *Effective Care Co-Ordination in Mental Health Services Modernising the Care Programme Approach* London: HMSO

George, E, Iveson, C, & Ratner, H (1998) *Problem to Solution: Brief Therapy with Individuals and Families* (revised) London: BT Press

George, E, Iveson, C, & Ratner, H (1997) *Training notes* (unpublished)

Gray, JM (1998) Putting Occupation Into Practice: Occupation as Ends, Occupation as Means *American Journal of Occupational Therapy* (52) 5

Kielhofner, G (2002) *A Model of Human Occupation: Theory and Application.* 3rd ed. Baltimore: Williams and Wilkins

Labour Force Survey 1997/8 *Unemployment and Activity Rates for People of Working Age* in Department for Education and Employment (1998) *Background Paper for Welfare to Work Seminar* DFEE: London

Metcalf, L (1998) *Solution Focused Group Therapy: ideas for groups in private practice, school, agencies, and treatment programs* New York: The Free Press

Pierce, D (2001a) Untangling Occupation and Activity *The American Journal of Occupational Therapy* 55(2) 138-146

Pierce, D (2001b) Occupation by Design: Dimensions, Therapeutic Power, and Creative Process *The American Journal of Occupational Therapy* 55(3) 249-259

O'Connell, B (2001) *Solution Focused Stress Counselling* London: Sage

Rebeiro, KL and Cook, JV (1999) Opportunity not Prescription: An exploratory study of the Experience of Occupational Engagement *Canadian Journal of Occupational Therapy* 66(4) 176-184

Reilly, M (1962) Occupational Therapy Can Be One of the Great Ideas of 20th-century Medicine *American Journal of Occupational Therapy* (16) 1-9

Roberts, G and Wolfson, P (2004) The Rediscovery of Recovery: Open to All *Advances in Psychiatric Treatment* (10) 37-49

Rose, D (2001) *Users' Voices: The Perspective of Mental Health Service Users on Community and Hospital Care* London: The Sainsbury Centre for Mental Health

Sayce, L (2000) From Psychiatric Patient to Citizen: Overcoming Discrimination and Social Exclusion Basingstoke: Macmillan Press

Social Exclusion Unit (2003) Mental Health and Social Exclusion Scoping Note Available from: http://www.socialexclusionunit. gov.uk/mental_health/MH_scoping_note.doc

Sumsion, T (1999a) Overview of Client-Centred Practice in Sumsion, T (1999) Client-Centred Practice in Occupational Therapy London: Churchill Livingstone

Sumsion, T (1999b) Implementation Issues in Sumsion, (1999) Client-Centred Practice in Occupational Therapy London: Churchill Livingstone

Tohn, SL and Oshlag, JA (1997) Crossing the Bridge: Integrating Solution Focused Therapy into Clinical Practice Sudbury: Solutions Press

Warner, L (2000) Out at Work: A survey of the experiences of people with mental health problems within the workplace London: Mental Health Foundation

Wilcock, A (1998) An Occupational Perspective of Health Thorofare: Slack

About the Authors

Lucie Duncan is currently working as a Head Occupational Therapist and Group Coordinator in South Kent. She qualified as an Occupational Therapist from St. Andrews Hospital, Northampton (Leicester University) in 1995. Since qualifying she has specialised in mental health work. She has worked in a variety of settings including a community older adult team and an acute adult in-patient unit. Her main practice area has been community adult mental health.

Since discovering solution focused practice her work as an occupational therapist has evolved and developed considerably. She has been able to enhance her occupational therapy skills and work more collaboratively and successfully with service users.

Rayya Ghul is senior lecturer in occupational therapy at Canterbury Christ Church University, where she has worked since 2000. She qualified from the London School of Occupational Therapy in 1982. She has worked in a variety of mental health settings in London, Reading and more recently, East Kent. She also worked for some time promoting arts for disabled people with Shape London.

In 1997 she attended a solution focused brief training course at the Brief Therapy Practice and began to apply a solution focus to her work in mental health services with exciting and sometimes surprising results. Since then she has been interested in developing ways of integrating a solution focus into occupational therapy and other health and social care professions and processes.

Rayya has been involved in training for some years and provided courses in solution focused brief therapy for East Kent NHS Trusts. She has taught solution focused brief therapy at the University of Kent at Canterbury and the Institute of Psychiatry in London. She has consulted with teams to develop solution focused practice in a range of health and social care settings, both physical and mental health. She has presented on integrating a solution focused approach at national and international conferences.

Sarah Mousley has worked as an occupational therapist for 10 years. She qualified in 1992 from Dorset House of Occupational Therapy, Oxford.

She has specialised in the field of mental health, working in a variety of settings including community mental health teams, residential and rehabilitation services and a day hospital. At time of publication she has been taking a break from her career to bring up her children.

On discovering solution focused therapy, she found that looking at clients' strengths and resources seemed to fit naturally with the vision of occupational therapy. She has been incorporating these ideas into her work ever since, finding the process creative and inspiring.

We hope that you have found the ideas in this book useful and inspiring. When we talk together about the difference a solution focus has made to our work as occupational therapists in mental health services, the most important aspect for all of us has been the shift from seeing our clients as walking problems, diagnoses or even as potential risks, to seeing them as people with strengths and resources, hopes and dreams, and possibilities for a positive future.

> "A pile of rocks ceases to be a rock pile when somebody contemplates it with the idea of a cathedral."
>
> Antoine de Saint-Exupery

Lucie Duncan   **Rayya Ghul**   **Sarah Mousley**

This book has been written over many cups of tea! Many biscuits and cakes have been consumed but our favourite, and the one that has provided us with the most brain power is the following:

Flapjacks

Heat 6oz butter/margarine with 1oz syrup in a saucepan until melted. Add 4oz soft brown sugar, 8oz porridge oats, 2oz desiccated coconut and 1 teaspoon ground ginger. Stir until all ingredients are combined. Put into a greased tin (approx 12" x 7")

Cook for 15 minutes at 180°C

Cut into squares whilst warm

Leave in tin to cool

Best enjoyed without a book to write